Green Line 5

Workbook

von
Jennifer Baer-Engel
Geraldine Greenhalgh
Jon Marks
Alison Wooder

Ernst Klett Verlag
Stuttgart · Leipzig

Across cultures 1

VOCABULARY

1 Fact file: The United Kingdom → SB 10

What do you remember about the UK? Complete the fact file.

UNITED KINGDOM
Population: 66.4 million (22nd in the world); **Area:** 242,500 km²

Interesting facts: The full name of the UK is United Kingdom of _Great_ Britain and Northern _Ireland_. It includes _Wales_, Scotland, _England_ and Northern Ireland. Almost everyone in the UK speaks English, but there are other regional languages too, for example, _Welsh_ in Wales, Scottish Gaelic in Scotland, Irish Gaelic in _Northern Ireland_ and Cornish in _____. The UK is the world's sixth largest _country_, and the second largest in Europe after Germany. In a _election_ in June 2016, the British people voted 52% to 48% to leave the _EU_. This decision became known as *Brexit*.

Facts and figures on this page are based on data 2017–2019

VOCABULARY

2 More about the Commonwealth → SB 10

a) *Complete this text about the Commonwealth.*

There are 54 countries in the Commonwealth, making it home to 2.4 _billion_ people. Its beginning goes back to the British Empire. The British didn't treat indigenous populations, like the _Aboriginal people_, well. Back then _racism_ was widespread. Also, they controlled the colonies economically, so many wanted to become _free and independent_. To keep the relationships among the former colonies and Britain, the Commonwealth was _invented_. India, whose political system is the largest _democratic_ in the world, was the first country that didn't have to accept the British _monarch_ as _head_ of state to become a member of the Commonwealth. This change led to many other former colonies joining the association. The member states have common _civil rights_ like democracy and peace. South Africa had to leave the Commonwealth for almost 30 years because the other member states criticised the _politic_ system. This system, which was based on racial _segregation_, stood in contrast with the _democratic_ values of the association.

SPEAKING

b) *In groups of four, act out a role play: For a podcast, a journalist interviews three teenagers, who come from South Africa, India and Australia, about what it is like to live in their countries.*

Check-in 1

Unit 1 G'day Australia!

VOCABULARY

1 Organising vocabulary → SB 12

a) Some words often appear together. Use the words from the boxes to find useful phrases for describing a country. (There are several possible combinations.)

| average | climatic | household | mineral | + | areas | density | conditions | resources |
| natural | population | poverty | rural | urbanised | | wealth | debt | income | line | beauty |

real income, poverty line, mineral areas, natural resources, average income, average debt, climatic areas, urbanised area, household income/debt,

b) After a year abroad in Australia, you write a social media post (about 100 words) about Australia as a country of contrasts. Write in your exercise book and use at least four of the phrases.

WRITING

2 A quiz: Interesting facts about Australia → SB 12; S1

a) How much do you know about Australia? Complete the quiz questions and tick ✓ the correct answer. (Compare your answers with the solutions on p. 72.)

1. *How many* sheep are there *per* person in Australia?
   a) ☐ 12 b) ☒ 8 c) ☐ 6

2. Australia has the *longest* national highway *~~of the~~* world. How many kilometres is this important road?
   a) ☐ 32,400 b) ☒ 14,500 c) ☐ 10,400

3. The outback covers 70 % *percentage* continent, so a large part of the *population* lives on the coast. What is the correct *~~twentie~~* ?
   a) ☒ 90 % b) ☐ 85 % c) ☐ 70 %

4. *Wich* animals in Australia kill the most *people* each year?
   a) ☐ snakes b) ☐ bees
   c) ☒ horses and cows ✓

5. Since *~~~~* have Aboriginal people *~~twedwhen~~ long* in Australia?
   a) ☒ 60,000 to 40,000 BC
   b) ☐ 7,000 years ago
   c) ☐ since the dinosaurs

6. The Great Barrier Reef is the *biggest* coral reef in the world. It is nearly *so* long *as* the distance *from berlin* Neuschwanstein Castle and which city?
   a) ☐ Reykjavík b) ☐ New York
   c) ☒ Moscow

b) Do some research and write three more quiz questions on Australia. Exchange your quiz with a partner.

three 3

1 Station 1

LISTENING

3 Where to go in Australia → SB 15; S12

A1 🔊

a) *Listen to the conversation between an Australian and two British tourists at the airport. Tick ✔ the correct statement(s).*

1. ☐ The British tourists have planned their holiday in Australia very well.
2. ☐ Because Australia is so big, the tourists should go by plane.
3. ☒ It's better not to try and see too much because you might lose too much time travelling.
4. ☒ Bondi Beach is not a good place for swimming in July.

b) *Underline the correct answers. Sometimes more than one answer is correct.*

1. In Sydney, the tourists should visit <u>the Museum of Sydney.</u> | <u>the Opera House.</u> | <u>the Royal Botanic Garden</u>.
2. The Rocks is where surfing was invented. | Australia declared its independence. | <u>the first Europeans settled.</u>
3. The Australian suggests visiting <u>Eaglereach.</u> | <u>Uluru.</u> | Kings Canyon.

c) *Answer the questions. Take notes.*

1. Why is Brisbane a good place to visit? warm, swim in sea, beach wake your interesting
2. What's the best way to travel to Brisbane? More overnight train

LANGUAGE

4 Tourists in Australia → SB 15; G1

Some tourists have posted about their holiday plans. Complete the posts.
*Use the **simple present** and the **present progressive**.*

Example: diving tour (tomorrow) | start: 8 a.m. | meeting point: on the beach

Rishi: I'm doing a diving tour at the Great Barrier Reef tomorrow. The tour starts at 8 a.m. We're meeting on the beach.

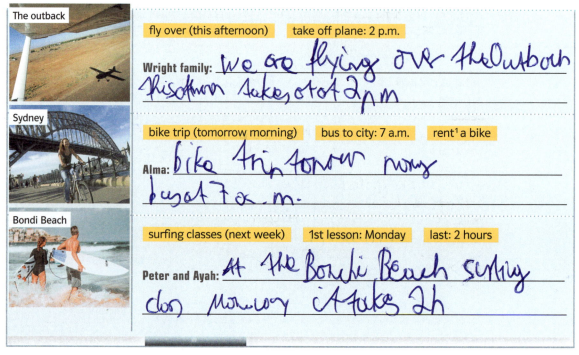

The outback
fly over (this afternoon) | take off plane: 2 p.m.
Wright family: We are flying over the Outback this afternoon takes off at 2 p.m.

Sydney
bike trip (tomorrow morning) | bus to city: 7 a.m. | rent¹ a bike
Alma: bike trip tomorrow morning bus at 7 a.m.

Bondi Beach
surfing classes (next week) | 1st lesson: Monday | last: 2 hours
Peter and Ayah: At the Bondi Beach surfing class Monday it takes 2h

¹ to rent [rent] *mieten*

Station 1

5 Travel plans → SB 16; G2

a) For your holiday in Australia next month, you've planned out different activities. Write down what you will be doing Monday to Sunday. Add two or three own ideas.

`take a surfing lesson`   `dive with great white sharks`   `go on a guided tour`   `have a barbie`   `visit Uluru`

On Monday I'll be visiting Sydney Aquarium. On Tuesday I'll _____

_____

_____

_____

_____

_____

b) A lot of students do a gap year in a foreign country like Australia. Think about which countries you would like to travel to. Partner A describes what he / she will be doing there. Partner B has to guess where partner A wants to go. Take turns.

Example: **A:** I'll be wearing a bikini and I'll be going to the beach every day. I'll be learning how to surf and dive. I'll be celebrating Christmas in summer. – **B:** You want to travel to Australia.

6 Find the mistakes: Down Under → SB 16; G1, G3–4

Read a German backpacker's blog post about his plans for his trip to Australia. Decide if the underlined phrases are correct or not. Correct the mistakes.

This time, next month, my plane (1) <u>will have landed</u> in Australia. I'm (2) <u>excited really</u> about this adventure trip! It'll be my first time to visit 'Down Under'. My plane (3) <u>leave</u> on 25th December. That's right, (4) <u>I'm flying</u> to Australia on Christmas Day! This trip (5) <u>was going to be</u> my Christmas present to (6) <u>me</u>. I (7) <u>planned</u> this trip for a year now. The first place (8) <u>I'm going visit</u> is Cairns, in Queensland. I'm staying in the youth hostel there because it's cheap and it sounds (9) <u>very comfortably</u>.

The weather forecast says (10) <u>it's going to be</u> very warm in December so I want to go swimming around the Great Barrier Reef. After this, (11) <u>I'm visit</u> Daintree, a national park (12) <u>where</u> you can go on different bushwalking trails. There are bushwalking guides (13) <u>which</u> (14) <u>took</u> tourists on walks at regular times. If I'm lucky, I (15) <u>would see</u> some cute koalas. Of course, it's important to (16) <u>beware</u> of any (17) <u>dead</u> animals. If I (18) <u>would be bitten</u> by a venomous snake, my next journey would be to hospital by air ambulance. Then I (19) <u>would have cancelled</u> the rest of my adventure when I had only just started! I (20) <u>write</u> more about my plans for my fantastic adventure Down Under soon.

Station 1

VOCABULARY

7 A news report on a crocodile attack → SB 16

a) *Read the news report on a crocodile attack. Underline the correct words.*

A British tourist in Australia has been attacked by saltwater crocodiles, known locally as 'salties'. The tourist, Nathan Berkley (23), who was staying at a **close / nearby / near** youth **association / hostel / hotel**, was with a group of friends on the beach. They were enjoying a barbie **when / then / during** Nathan decided to go for a walk on his own. He got lost, and went further and further from the beach **as far as / until / up to** he accidentally[1] **frightened / bothered / disturbed** some crocs. "It was really scary," said Nathan. "I was walking down a little **track / way / direction** by a river. Suddenly, I noticed I walked into a whole **cluster / team / collection** of crocs. They **raced / chased / hunted** me, and they're surprisingly fast. I escaped, but not before I'd been **bitten / stung / grabbed** quite badly on one leg."

b) *Take turns and explain what the other words mean. You can use a dictionary for help.*

c) *Think of a suitable heading for the article.* _____

LANGUAGE

8 Mixed bag: Australia's dangerous animals → SB 16; G4

Complete this text about Australia's most dangerous animals.

Australia is famous for some of ___the deadliest___ (deadly) animals in the world. ___There are___ so much about hungry sharks, venomous jellyfish and snakes can make you worry, but that doesn't mean you should avoid ___the visity___ Australia's beaches. It's also comforting ___place to hear___ that only 1.1 people die ___per___ year from a shark ___attack___. Also, if you ___don't___ (not want) ___be stung___ by ___stay by___ box jellyfish, you need to swim at beaches that ___nested___ off. The nets stop the dangerous jellyfish from ___getting___ close to the coastline. So far, there ___were only___ (only) 69 deaths since 1883. The aggressive brown snake ___responsible___ for the most deaths by snake bite. But you can ___get saved___ (save) if you get an ambulance and hospital help ___in___ time. Of ___course___ not all animals in Australia are deadly and even if you come across one, it's unlikely that it ___will bite kill___ you.

SPEAKING

9 Stay safe in Australia → SB 16; S13

A tour guide is talking to a tourist about how to stay safe in Australia. Act out a role play.

Partner A:
You are a foreign tourist in Australia. Ask for advice about the following: sharks, jellyfish, rip currents, the sun, snakes, bushwalking.

Partner B:
You are an Australian tour guide. Give advice about safety for tourists in your country. Use what you have learned about this so far.

[1] accidentally [ˌæksɪˈdentli] zufällig, versehentlich

Station 1

MEDIATION 10 Work and travel → SB 17; S13, S15

a) *Deine schwedische Freundin Nina, die gerade ihren Abschluss gemacht hat und mit der du dir auf Englisch schreibst, will ein Jahr nach Australien. Sie muss aber noch ihre Eltern überzeugen. Diese glauben unter anderem, dass Work-and-Travel-Arbeitskräfte oft ausgenutzt werden. Schreibe ihr eine E-Mail (ca. 170 Wörter), in der du ihr die in dem Artikel genannten Vorteile eines Jahrs in Australien nennst, ihr aber auch aufzeigst, inwieweit ihre Eltern recht haben.*

Nach dem Abi ins Outback

Für viele Schülerinnen und Schüler stellt sich spätestens nach dem Abitur die Frage „Was kommt als Nächstes?". Für die damals noch 18-jährige Abiturientin Emma war die Antwort schnell klar: „Die meisten meiner Freunde haben den Umzug an ihren Studienort geplant. Ich wollte lieber was anderes machen." Die Entscheidung, für ein Jahr nach Australien zu reisen, ist ihr nicht sehr schwergefallen, denn Australien ist nicht nur ein faszinierendes Land, sondern macht Backpackern die Einreise besonders einfach. „Man findet auf Blogs von anderen Reisenden eigentlich alle Infos, die man braucht", erklärt Emma und empfiehlt ein Working Holiday Visum, das man online beantragen und mit dem man sogar bis zu drei Jahre in Australien wohnen und arbeiten kann.

Ihre ersten Wochen in Australien hat Emma in Sydney verbracht. Die inzwischen 23-Jährige erzählt, dass sie am Anfang Schwierigkeiten mit der Sprache hatte. „An australisches Englisch gewöhnt man sich irgendwann, aber viel herausfordernder ist es, wenn man in Hostels dann auch noch auf Leute aus aller Welt trifft. Mich auf die verschiedenen Akzente einzustellen, hat mir sehr geholfen, mein Englisch zu verbessern."

Ihren ersten Job hat Emma als Kellnerin in einer Bar ergattert. „Die Bezahlung war sehr gut und ich hatte flexible Arbeitszeiten. So hatte ich immer noch genug Freizeit, um mich mit meinen neuen Freunden zu treffen." Emma hatte Glück, denn sie erhielt bei ihrer Arbeit den Mindestlohn, der in Australien sehr hoch ist. Vor allem in der Gastronomie kann es aber passieren, dass die Arbeitgeber die Flexibilität der Backpacker ausnutzen, um den Mindestlohn zu umgehen. Trotz gutem Gehalt konnte Emma in dieser Zeit nicht viel Geld ansparen, denn sie arbeitete nur in Teilzeit und in Sydney „gibt es einfach zu viele Möglichkeiten, Geld auszugeben", wie sie zugibt. „Und das Ziel meiner Reise war es ja nicht, am Ende mit einem vollen Konto nach Hause zu kommen, sondern mir die Reise zu finanzieren."

„Als mir zwei Freundinnen vorschlugen, mit ihnen im Campervan weiterzureisen, sagte ich sofort zu. Nach drei Wochen Abenteuerurlaub war aber klar, dass ich wieder Geld verdienen musste." Sie fing als *fruit picker* auf einer Farm im australischen Queensland an. „Die Arbeit war wirklich hart. Wir mussten bei 40 Grad im Schatten acht Stunden am Tag Olivenbäume beschneiden", berichtet Emma. Doch nicht nur das. Die Unterkunft war eine einfache Hütte ohne Bad, eine Internetverbindung war kaum vorhanden und an zwei Tagen fiel auch noch das Wasser aus. Sie blieb trotzdem für einen Monat, denn „irgendwie gehört das zum Backpacken in Australien dazu", erläutert Emma mit einem Lachen.

Zusammen mit einem anderen Backpacker ging es als *farm hand* auf einer Rinderfarm tiefer in den Outback. Die Arbeit war zwar auch körperlich anstrengend, aber sie hat dort vieles gelernt, wie z. B. Motorrad fahren und Bäume fällen. Die Weite und Einsamkeit der Landschaft haben Emma fasziniert und sie blieb drei Monate. Was Emma am meisten an ihrem Jahr in Australien schätzt, sind nicht die Abenteuer, die sie erlebt hat, sondern das Gefühl vollkommener Unabhängigkeit. Emma betont, dass sie „jedem, der mit dem Gedanken spielt Work and Travel in Australien zu machen", diese Erfahrung empfehlen kann.

SPEAKING b) *What do you think: Would you like to do work and travel in Australia? Discuss with a partner.*

…

Station 2

11 A convict's story → SB 18; S12

LISTENING A2

a) You are in a museum in Australia. At a display you press a button to hear more about a convict called William Buckley. Listen and put the events in the correct order. There are two extra sentences.

- 2 A. [x] He escaped from a prison camp.
- 1 B. [x] He was arrested and sent to Australia.
- 6 C. [x] The *Life and Adventures of William Buckley* was published.
- 4 D. [x] He spent 32 years with an Aboriginal tribe.
- E. [ ] He worked as a writer.
- 3 F. [x] He survived on his own in the wilderness.
- 5 G. [x] He went back to the British colony.
- H. [ ] He was attacked by the Wathaurung.

b) Listen again and tick ✓ the correct answers.

1. Why was Buckley arrested?
   - a) [ ] He had stolen something.
   - b) [x] He was carrying stolen objects. ✓
   - c) [ ] The reason is not known.

2. How long did the journey to Australia last?
   - a) [x] 6 months ✓
   - b) [ ] 14 months
   - c) [ ] 22 months

c) Answer these questions. Take notes.

1. Why did very few convicts try to escape from the prison camp? _To live a new life outside was even worse_

2. What did Buckley do after he had left the Wathaurung tribe? _Went back to the British colony, lived in Sidney, told his story_

12 The terrible effects of Australia's colonial times → SB 19; G5

LANGUAGE

Find verbs to complete this text about Australia Day. Use the correct tenses (**simple past, present perfect** or **present perfect progressive**), active or passive.

Since 1935 Australians _have been celebrating_ 'Australia Day' every year on the 26th January, the day the British arrived in 1788. However, for many indigenous Australians whose ancestors _arrived in_ colonial times and the death and disease it _brought_ to their people, there might seem very little to celebrate. Australia's indigenous people _are celebrated/praising_ their traditions for tens of thousands of years. When the first Europeans _came_ in the 17th century, the lives of indigenous people _left_ forever. Many _settler die_ from European diseases and in the violent fights against Europeans who _decided_ to take their land. Indigenous people _has been accepted_ as Australian citizens with full rights only since 1967. So it's no surprise that up until now many indigenous Australians _had been protesting_ against Australia Day instead of celebrating it.

Station 2

LANGUAGE 13 Surprising things happen → SB 19; G5

For your travel blog you collected stories and pictures about surprising and shocking things that happened to people during their holiday in Australia. Write the captions for these photos. Use the **past progressive** for the background situation and the **simple past** for the action. Link the clauses with **while** or **when**.

Example: A koala was eating leaves in a tree when he lost his balance and fell.

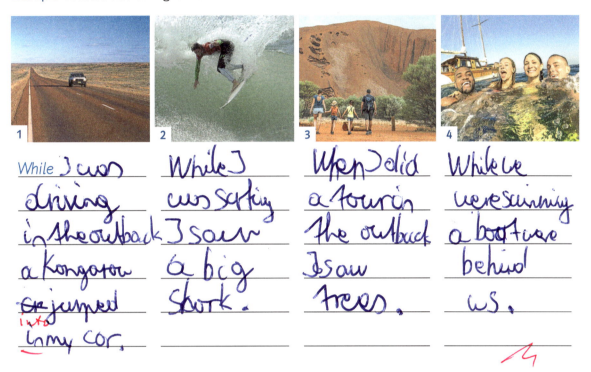

1. While I was driving in the outback a kangaroo jumped into my car.

2. While I was surfing I saw a big shark.

3. When I did a tour in the outback I saw trees.

4. While we were swimming a boat was behind us.

LANGUAGE 14 An e-mail from Australia → SB 19; G6

Tania and her mum are on holiday in Australia. Complete Tania's e-mail to a friend with these verbs. Be careful with simple and progressive forms of stative and dynamic verbs.

be | have (4x) | look (2x) | see | taste | think (2x) | wish

Hi Malika, we _are having_ a wonderful time here in Oz. Except for one thing: Mum _has_ a terrible fear of snakes. Yesterday we _were having_ a barbie on the beach when Mum suddenly pointed to the ground and cried, "Can you _see_ that?" But it _was_ only a lizard – no snakes anywhere near us! The food also _tastes_ different here. It must be the sea air! I _wish_ we could stay in Australia longer. Australians are so friendly! I have even made some new friends. One of them, Oliver, always _has_ something funny to say and he _looks_ great too! I'm sure that at the barbie, he _looks_ in my direction all evening 😊. Actually, I _am thinking_ about coming back and doing a gap year here. Maybe you would like to come too? What _do_ you _think_? Lots of love, Tania

Station 2

15 **The life of an Australian firefighter** → SB 19; G5–6

Lucas is talking about his job as a firefighter. Complete the text with the correct verb forms.

G'day, my name's Lucas, I __am__ a firefighter in Victoria, Australia. My career as a firefighter first __started__ when I __joined__ (join) our local fire service as a volunteer. I __had just__ (just celebrate) my 16th birthday a few days before.

I __have been fighting__ (fight) fires for 10 years now and I __have seen__ (see) some scary scenes, believe me! But I love my job and I guess I __'ll still be working__ (still work) as a firefighter ten years from now. Unfortunately, bushfires __are__ very common here, especially in summer. Because the earth __is getting__ warmer and warmer each year, these fires __will increase__ (increase¹) in the future. These fires also __kill__ (kill) huge numbers of wildlife. But of course, firefighting __has__ some wonderful moments too, which I know I __'ll never forget__ (never forget).

16 **What kind of visa?** → SB 20; G7

Complete this answer to an online forum question with a suitable form of **let, allow, make (sb do sth)** or **have (sth done)**.

Question 17:32

I want to travel around Australia for a few months, but I'll need to earn some money when I'm there. Should I get some kind of visa before I go?

Answer 17:35

Yes! The Australian Government only __allows__ foreign people who have the correct type of visa to work in Australia. I think you'll need the type I applied for. It's called a Working Holiday Visa. With one of those, the government __lets/allows__ you to live and work in Australia for up to 12 months. They won't __let__ you work for any one company for more than six months, so it's best for people who want to combine work with travelling. It's best to apply online (they'll __make__ you pay more if you apply by mail). They __make__ you answer a lot of questions when you first apply, and you must __have__ your health checked by a doctor, but after that it's quite quick and easy.

¹ to increase [ɪnˈkriːs] zunehmen

Station 2

17 Travelling on your own → SB 20; G7

Complete what these teenagers posted about travelling on their own.
Use **let, allow, make** or **have** and your own ideas.

1. My parents say I'm too young, so they _don't allow me to go to the party_.

2. I thought working at a restaurant would be fun, but my boss _makes me clean_.

3. I thought it would be a great idea to travel with my best friend, but he always gets in the bathroom first and _never leaves it soon, makes me wait_.

4. Even though my parents are very worried about me, they _think I'm not ready_ _~~told me~~ are having a_

18 Talking about diagrams → SB 21; S17

a) Look at the diagram and complete the text that introduces it.

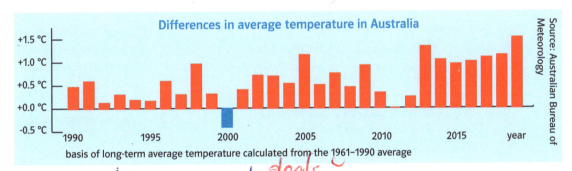

The diagram is a ~~column~~ **bar** graph which ~~shows~~ **deals** with the change in average temperature in _Australia_ between _1990_ and 2019. It shows the _difference_ between the long-term average temperature and the ~~average~~ **actual** yearly temperature in _degree_ Celsius. The diagram _is based_ on data by the _Australian Bureau of Meteorology_.

b) In your exercise book, write four to five sentences which describe the most important figures and developments in the diagram.

Useful phrases

The diagram clearly shows … | The difference between … has gone up significantly | … has (not) increased … since … | … almost always over … | … the highest increase so far.

c) Think about what reasons there might be for the increasing temperatures and what problems this development might create in Australia. Write a short text (about 150 words) in your exercise book. Use these prompts or your own ideas.

bushfire   drought[1]   farms   health   sea temperature

1 drought [draʊt] Dürre

1 Station 2 Station 3

VOCABULARY **19** **Aussie talk** → SB 21

Tyler is visiting his friend Jackie in Australia. Use Australian English phrases to complete the dialogue.

Jackie: G'day, mate! _____?

Tyler: I'm fine thanks. I slept like a baby. Must be the heat.

Jackie: By the way, are these _____? I found them behind the couch.

Tyler: Oh, yes! I've been looking for those flip-flops everywhere. Thanks a lot!

Jackie: _____.

Tyler: I'm so hungry! What's for breakfast?

Jackie: Well all kinds _____. We've got eggs, tomatoes and …

READING **20** **Jokes** → SB 21

Read the jokes. In pairs talk about whether these jokes would work in German too. Explain why/why not.

1. What do you give a kangaroo when it's ill?
⇒ A hoperation.

2. How do you get rid of a boomerang?
⇒ You throw it down a one-way street.

3. What do you call a boomerang that won't come back? ⇒ A stick.

4. What do sea monsters eat? ⇒ Fish and ships.

LANGUAGE **21** **Changing attitudes** → SB 23; G8

Complete the text about the treatment of Aboriginal people with **(not) used to** and these verbs.

~~be~~   ~~treat~~   ~~experience~~   ~~force~~   take   ~~have~~   ~~work~~

The colonial government _used to treat_ Aboriginal people very badly. They _used to have_ the same rights as white people, and they often _work_ for little or no money. The government _used to take_ children with one Aboriginal and one white parent from their homes and send them to white families or children's homes. Mining companies _used to force_ Aboriginal people to leave their land. There _used to be_ any Aboriginal politicians in the government.

These are just a few examples of the discrimination Aboriginal people _____.

Station 3

SPEAKING **22** **The good old days** → SB 23; G8

Imagine you're 80 and look back on your life today. Talk to your partner about how things **used/didn't use to** be and the things you **would (not)** do. Think of free time, transportation, school or trends.

Example: When I was 15, we used to go swimming in the lake every summer. We would take our bikes and play music on our smartphones. We wouldn't go to virtual concerts back then.

VOCABULARY **23** **The early colonial years** → SB 23

Complete the text about Australia's early colonial years. Use synonyms (=), opposites (↔) or other related words (→) for the words in blue.

For nearly _centuries_ ✓ (= a hundred years), Britain sent many of its _criminals_ ✓ (→ crime) to Australia. Most of them had been sentenced for stealing small things such as clothes or food. They were _punished_ (→ punishment) with living in an Australian penal colony for a number of years. Many of them ~~decided~~ _chose_ (→ choice) to stay in Australia after they _had finished_ (↔ to start) their sentences. The early British _settlers_ ✓ (→ to settle) saw their presence in Australia as the colonisation of a _strange_ (= weird) new land. The Aboriginal people _of course_ (= obviously) viewed it as an invasion of their land by strange new people. For many years, the indigenous Australians _were oppressed_ (↔ to let sb live in freedom) by the _restrictive_ (→ to restrict) British laws against their language and culture. These unfair _historical_ (→ history) actions are still a reason for _bitterness_ (↔ sweetness), and many people feel that there's still discrimination in Australian society today.

MEDIATION **24** **The true effects of the white settlers in Australia** → SB 24; S2, S15

a) Read the article and do the exercises on the following page.

In 1788, eleven British ships arrived in Botany Bay in Sydney, with hundreds of convicts, several crew members and some British citizens. Their arrival was the start of the
5   oppression and destruction of the indigenous people who had been living in Australia for tens of thousands of years. Before the British landed, there were about 750,000 Aboriginal people living on the continent. Ten years after
10 the British had colonized the country, the effects were devastating, and the population was reduced by 90%.
    When the colonists landed on shore, they brought with them diseases that the Aboriginal people weren't used to and which resulted in the deaths of thousands of Aboriginal Australians.
    Although it was obvious that Australia was already inhabited, the British invaders established a policy that meant the land belonged to no one. This was called 'terra nullius' – in other words, 'empty continent'. As a consequence, many more Aboriginal people were killed as the British set up more settlements around the country to support their growing white population.
    In the past, the Aboriginal people had always lived in perfect balance with nature,

1 Station 3

moving around with the seasons, and hunting
and gathering food. However, the new settlers
ignored their way of life and traditions as
they grabbed more land for themselves.
This destruction of the Aboriginal people's
territories made it difficult for them to survive.
Many Aboriginal people wouldn't give up their
land easily and this led to further deaths as
violent conflicts took place between the two
groups.
    Not only did these brutal invaders threaten
the physical survival of indigenous groups,
they also threatened the survival of their
culture and spiritual traditions. One obvious
example of this is the renaming of Aboriginal
places. In the past, if you knew the place
names and how they were connected,
you could navigate your way around the
country. During colonisation, British explorers
replaced many of the Aboriginal names with
the names of then important white people in
the country or the names of famous British
people who had never even seen Australia.
Uluru is an example of a sacred Aboriginal
site that was renamed in 1873 after a British
colonial government official and businessman
in Australia at that time, Henry Ayers.
    Australia's dark history hasn't been dealt
with well; however, a national reconciliation
programme has been started. Australia still
has a lot of work to do to reconcile indigenous
and non-indigenous peoples, but it is showing
progress.

b) *Find words in the text that have the same meaning. Give the lines.*

1. highly damaging: _____   2. coast: _____

c) *Choose the correct answer to show that you understand these words and phrases from the text.*

1. Reconciliation means
   a) ☐ becoming friends again after an argument.
   b) ☐ speaking about forgotten events of the past.
   c) ☐ meeting someone again after a very long time.

2. To show progress means
   a) ☐ moving in different directions.
   b) ☐ improving constantly.
   c) ☐ accepting different opinions.

d) *Für ein Geschichtsprojekt zum Thema Kolonialisierung willst du aufzeigen, welche Folgen die britische Kolonialisierung für die Aborigines hatte und wie das Land heute mit dieser Vergangenheit umgeht. Nutze den Artikel und mache dir auf Deutsch Notizen für vier prompt cards.*

LANGUAGE **25** **Find the mistakes: Racism. It stops with me** → SB 24; G5, G8

Read the text about racism in football. Look at the underlined words and decide if they are correct or not. Correct the mistakes.

'Racism. It stops with me,' these are the powerful words of Adam Goodes. Adam (1) <u>used to being</u> one of the best footballers in Australia, until his life changed (2) <u>complete</u> when (3) <u>the</u> 13-year-old girl called him an ape[1] during one of his games. Goodes pointed at the girl who then (4) <u>had to leaving</u> and wasn't allowed back in the stadium. (5) <u>Although</u> Adam (6) <u>had been</u> the victim of that racist comment as an indigenous Australian, (7) <u>the medias</u> criticised him for not just (8) <u>ignoring</u> the comment. (9) <u>Adams</u> punishment, however, went on (10) <u>since</u> years after the event. During games in the stadium, the audiences booed him and (11) <u>finally 2015,</u> he (12) <u>was giving up</u> professional football. If it (13) <u>wouldn't have been</u> for that racist comment, he might still be playing football today. However, he (14) <u>always will continue</u> the fight for indigenous people's rights.

[1] ape [eɪp] *Affe*

SKILLS **26** A presentation handout → SB 26; S14

a) *Read the handout and do the exercises on the following page. You can use a dictionary for help.*

THE BLUE MOUNTAINS NATIONAL PARK, AUSTRALIA

1. GEOGRAPHY
- sandstone plateau
- natural features: cliffs, canyons, waterfalls, caves, forests
- typical flora (esp. eucalyptus) and fauna (e.g. cockatoos, wallabies)

2. TOURISM
- most visited National Park in NSW (almost 5.2 million visitors in 2016)
- largest visitor groups are from Sydney and NSW (almost 90 % in 2016)
- certified 'Ecotourism Destination'
- Aboriginal culture: rock art / stone paintings in Red Hands Cave
- activities for visitors: walking, cycling, visiting waterfalls, having a barbecue, rock climbing, canoeing, learning about flora and fauna, swimming, paddling, abseiling, canyoning, bush camping, bushwalking, scenic drives, wilderness training
- touristic highlights: Three Sisters rock formation, Grose Valley, Wentworth Falls

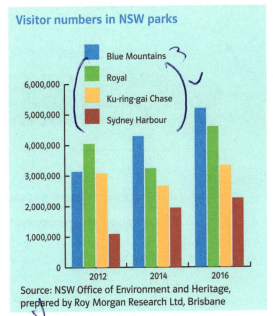

Source: NSW Office of Environment and Heritage, prepared by Roy Morgan Research Ltd, Brisbane

3. CURRENT CHALLENGES
The bushfires in late 2019 and early 2020 have caused huge destruction in the park. Plants and wildlife were affected greatly. The economic loss for the NP itself, but also for the whole tourism sector in the area was huge. The economic situation became even worse with the global COVID-19 pandemic. Just like many other public places, the facilities of the park had to be shut, and no visitors were allowed.

4. FACTS AND FIGURES
- in New South Wales (NSW) on the east coast of Australia, around 60 km west of Sydney
- part of the Greater Blue Mountains World Heritage Area
- area: 2,680 km²
- largest cities in Australia (>50 % of overall population): Sydney, Melbourne, Brisbane, Perth, Adelaide

5. Conclusion
- supports nature conservation and ecotourism
- balance between high visitor numbers and preserving nature: ongoing challenge

Sources: Annual Vists to NSW National Parks & Reserves Report, Blue Mountains Fauna Inventory Project, Encyclopedia Britannica, NSW National Parks and Wildlife Service, Sydney Morning Herald, The Guardian, Wikipedia

1 Skills Story

b) *Read the tips for making a good presentation handout. Decide if they are dos or don'ts.*

	Do	Don't
1. Organise the topics in the same logical order that you talk about them in the presentation.	✓	
2. Include lots of text that gives your audience all the detailed information.		✓
3. Print out all your presentation slides and use that as your handout.		✓
4. Show lots of beautiful photos on your handout.		✓
5. Include charts, maps or photos that make your main ideas clearer.	✓	
6. Sum up the main points of the presentation at the end.	✓	

c) *Check the Presentation skills box in your student's book again. Then, have a closer look at the handout and find six things that should be improved. Say why they should be changed and then, if possible, improve them in the handout directly.*

d) *With a partner, discuss the things you liked about the handout. Give reasons.*

> **Useful phrases**
>
> The handout is professional/interesting/original. | I especially liked… because … | … was done very well because … | I thought it was great that … | … helps the reader to understand the topic better.

VOCABULARY 27 A funny scene in the classroom → SB 31

a) *Find suitable verbs to complete these collocations about situations in the classroom.*

1. to _____ out worksheets
2. to _____ one's voice
3. to _____ into laughter
4. to _____ one's eyebrows
5. to _____ a knock
6. to _____ confusion
7. to _____ determined to
8. to _____ home
9. to _____ at one's desk
10. to _____ into one's chair

b) *Use at least five of the collocations to write a story (about 130 words) about a funny scene that happened in your (or an imaginary) classroom.*

READING 28 Bushfire! → SB 31; S2, S4–5

a) *Read the story and do the exercises on the following page.*

"I think there's still a window open in the kitchen," said Melissa's mother from the sofa.

"OK, Mum," said Melissa, who was making her mum a cup of coffee, "I'll close it."

5   The smoke from the bushfire was getting worse. In the distance, she could hear firefighters in helicopters who were trying to put out the flames. It probably wouldn't work. Bushfires often continued until the next rain, or until they had burnt everything there was to 10 burn in the area. She closed the window.

Melissa hated bushfires. It meant you had to stay at home all day or go out, cough a lot, and when you came back you smelled like a bonfire. And just two days ago, everything had been so 15 nice. She, her mum and her best friends Lucy and Jade had driven out into the bush, and had a wonderful barbecue. OK, they had driven past several signs that were saying 'NO FIRES', but a barbecue isn't really a fire. The flames are always under control. And after they had tipped the glowing charcoal onto the ground, they had poured some water onto it. Nothing could have gone wrong with that.

...

Blake took a packet of cigarettes from a pocket in the car door.

"I can't believe you still have that disgusting habit," said his sister Jessie from the passenger seat. "And in the car too! I'd like to breathe some air in here, you know."

"Relax," said Blake and lit the cigarette. "I'll open the windows."

"Last time I came to visit you, you promised to give it up," said Jessie.

"Hmph," said Blake. They drove in silence for a while along the long, straight outback road. Blake drove on that road almost every day, and he knew every turn, tree and signpost. Today he was picking up his sister from the nearest airport, a day's drive away. His sister was right. He really should give up smoking. He would stop after he had finished that packet. Or the next packet. A cough from the passenger seat interrupted his thoughts.

"Having the windows open isn't helping," said Jessie. "It still stinks of smoke in here."

"I think that smoke is coming from outside," said Blake. "Look, I can see a bushfire over there. It's new. It wasn't there when I passed this spot the day before yesterday."

"*Another* one," said Jessie. "There seem to be more of them every year. Anyway, finish that horrible cigarette and close the window again, before more smoke comes in."

"OK," said Blake. He took a final puff and threw his cigarette out of the window.

"You're joking? What about the fire risk?" said Jessie.

"It's just a cigarette end and there aren't any trees near the side of the road. I've been doing it for years. *That's* not what causes bushfires."

...

Shannon got out of her car. She walked quickly to the store. The automatic doors opened and closed.

"That's better," she said to the young man at the till. "You're lucky you've got good air-conditioning in here. It's getting hard to breathe out there."

"I hear the fire's only a couple of kilometres from the town now," said the man. "D'you think we'll have to evacuate, like we did a couple of years ago?"

"I hope not," said Shannon. She picked up a six pack of Orange Fizztastic and took it to the till.

"Five ninety-five," said the man. "I wonder what caused it this time."

An image appeared in Shannon's head. Two days earlier she had been walking home from the store instead of driving. She had taken a bottle of Fizztastic from her shopping bag, drunk it and then thrown the empty bottle into the bush. Of course, dropping litter was bad, but there was already quite a lot of it along that track. One more bottle wouldn't make any difference. A glass bottle ... Glass bottles can act as a magnifying glass. They focus the sun's rays into a point and start a ... No, that wasn't very likely.

"I said, I wonder what caused the fire this time," said the man.

"No idea," said Shannon. "Not me, anyway. I'm always super careful."

...

"This is Renee Brennan. I'm reporting live for KWA Radio. I'm standing about a kilometre away from one of the biggest bushfires this region has experienced. In the distance I can see firefighters in breathing equipment. They are cutting down the bush to try and stop the fire spreading, but with this wind that may not help very much. The nearby town of Locksville may have to be evacuated. With me here is Dean Collins of the local fire department. Dean, how bad is it?" Renee passed the microphone. "Very bad, Renee. I've not seen one this bad for a long time. Maybe never."

"Any idea what caused it?"

"No clue. But we think it started about two days ago in three separate places. One in a popular picnic spot out in the bush, one by the main road into Locksville and one on a track that leads from Locksville to some houses out in the bush."

Renee, who found it hard to breathe now, pointed the microphone back to her own mouth. It was time to go.

"Thanks, Dean. I'll let you get back to work. I apologise to you listeners at home, but the smoke is now so bad, we're gonna have to keep this report short and leave. So back to Taylor in the studio."

1 Story

b) *Find synonyms for these words in the text in parts 1 and 4. Give the lines.*

1. to empty out: _____   2. trash: _____

c) *Look at the words in the text and match them with the correct pictures.*

☐ charcoal (l. 22)   ☐ till (l. 66)   ☐ sun's rays (l. 87)
☐ passenger seat (ll. 28–29)   ☐ magnifying glass (l. 87)

1 2 3 4 5

d) *What is the story about? Complete the sentence.*

The story is about a _____ and is divided into _____ sections which show this event from different _____.

e) *Who does what in the story? Put in M for Melissa, B for Blake and S for Shannon. Sometimes it can be more than one person.*

1. ☐ ignores the signs on the way.
2. ☐ has a guilty conscience.
3. ☐ litters the environment.
4. ☐ can't give up a bad habit.
5. ☐ is lost in thought.
6. ☐ meets with friends.

f) *What are some of the problems the bushfire causes in the story? Choose the correct answers.*

1. ☐ There is a lot of air pollution.
2. ☐ The fire department doesn't have enough firefighters to handle a situation this bad.
3. ☐ Shops must close, and people must be evacuated immediately.
4. ☐ Bush is cut down to stop the fire from spreading.

g) *Complete the sentences.*

1. The turning point of the story is when _____
   _____

2. The message of the story is that _____

WRITING 29 An Australian story → SB 31; S6–8

○ *Choose **one** of the following tasks. Write about 150 words in your exercise book.*
○
○ 1. Write a news report on the bushfire from the story.
  2. Some bushfires in the Australian bush are started by campfires. Imagine a group of tourists are camping in the bush when their campfire gets out of control. What do they do? How do they react? Write a scene, including dialogue and stage directions and act it out.

Focus 1 Aotearoa – the 'land of the white cloud'

READING

1 Last chance to see → SB 33; S2, S4–8

a) In "Last Chance to see" writer Douglas Adams and zoologist Mark Carwardine travel around the world to see some of the world's most endangered[1] species before they might become extinct. At the time the book was published (1990) there were only about 40 kakapos left in New Zealand. Luckily, the population has grown to over 200 again. Read the excerpt and do the exercises.

The helicopter puts its nose down and goes thrumming its way along the canyon wall. We frighten a couple of birds. Mark quickly reaches under his seat for his binoculars.

"Keas!" he says. I nod but only very slightly. He follows them for a few seconds more, until they disappear from view. They are not what we have come to look for.

Until 1987 Fiordland was the home of one of the strangest, most unearthly sounds in the world. For thousands of years, in the right season, the sound could be heard after nightfall throughout these wild peaks and valleys.

It was like a heartbeat: a deep powerful throb that echoed through the dark. It was so deep that some people will tell you that they felt it in their stomach before they could identify the actual sound. Most people have never heard it at all, or ever will again. It was the sound of the kakapo, the old night parrot of New Zealand.

Of all the creatures we were searching for this year it was probably the strangest and most fascinating, and also one of the most hard to find. Once, before New Zealand was inhabited by humans, there were hundreds of thousands of kakapos. Then there were thousands, then hundreds. Then there were just forty … and counting.

Until relatively recently – in the evolutionary scale of things – the wildlife of New Zealand consisted of almost nothing but birds. Only birds could reach the place. The ancestors of many of the birds that are now natives of New Zealand originally flew here.

There were no predators. No dogs, no cats, or weasels, nothing that the birds needed to escape from. And flight of course, is a means of escape. It's a survival mechanism, and one that the birds of New Zealand found they didn't especially need.

So when European settlers arrived and brought cats and dogs and weasels and possums with them, a lot of New Zealand's flightless birds were suddenly waddling for their lives. The kiwis, the takahes – and the old night parrots, the kakapos.

Of these the kakapo is the strangest. It is an extremely fat bird. An adult will weigh about six or seven pounds, and its wings are just about good for waggling – but flying is completely out of the question. Sadly, however, it seems that not only has the kakapo forgotten how to fly, but it has also forgotten that it has forgotten how to fly. Apparently a seriously worried kakapo will sometimes run up a tree and jump out of it, at which point it flies like a brick and lands in an inelegant heap[2] on the ground.

However, the kakapo has never learned to worry. It's never had anything much to worry about. Its reaction when confronted with a predator is that it simply doesn't know what it's supposed to do. It has no conception of the idea that anything could possibly want to hurt it, so it just sits on its nest in a state of complete confusion and leaves the other animal to make the next move – which is usually a final one.

The trouble is that this predator business has happened rather suddenly in New Zealand, and soon there won't be any kakapos left at all, unless human intervention can protect them.

From: *Last Chance to see* by Douglas Adams and Mark Carwardine

1 endangered [ɪnˈdeɪndʒəd] gefährdet   2 heap [hiːp] Haufen

Focus 1

b) Find the words in the text for these definitions:

1. object used to look at things far away: _____

2. sound a heart makes: _____

3. way to get out of a dangerous situation: _____

4. to take action: _____

New Zealand

Fiordlands

c) Some of the words in the excerpt are similar to the sound or action they describe. Match them with the correct meaning.

1. to thrum (l. 2)
2. throb (l. 14)
3. to waddle (l. 43)
4. to waggle (l. 49)

a) to make small steps and move from side to side
b) a beat with a strong rhythm
c) to make a continuous sound
d) to move with short quick movements

d) Choose the statement which explains the phrase "in the evolutionary scale of things" (ll. 29–30) best.

1. ☐ Because evolution takes such a long time, years are counted differently.
2. ☐ Something that seems long ago to us isn't very long ago when it's viewed from the perspective of evolution.
3. ☐ The time it takes for animals to develop is different and depends on how big they are.

e) Name five characteristics which make the kakapo one of the strangest birds.

_____

_____

_____

f) Are these statements true, false or not in the text? Tick ✔ the correct answer.

	true	false	not in the text
1. Bats were the only animals which weren't birds that also flew to New Zealand.	☐	☐	☐
2. For a long time, there were no predators in New Zealand, so the birds didn't need to be able to fly to survive.	☐	☐	☐
3. The Maori brought predators to the islands.	☐	☐	☐

g) Underline the correct answer. Then underline examples in the excerpt that support your choice in 2.

1. The book belongs to the genre of … | travel guides. | adventure stories. | travel literature.
2. To make it more entertaining for the reader, the authors use … | suspense. | humour. | fiction.

WRITING

h) In your last post on your travel blog you wrote about the flightless birds of New Zealand. Think about at least three questions that your readers might have about the topic. Use the information from the excerpt to write an FAQ in your exercise book in which you answer their questions.

Focus 1

LISTENING

2 On location → SB 35; S12

a) *Listen to a radio show about film locations in New Zealand. Match the photos with the film locations and, in the boxes, say which film was shot there. Use **L** for Lord of the Rings, **P** for Pete's Dragon and **W** for Whale Rider. There is one extra photo.*

Hobbiton | Kaitoke | Rotorua | Tongariro | Whangara

1 _____ 2 _____ 3 _____

4 _____ 5 _____ 6 _____

b) *Listen again and complete the text.*

The _____ has had a big influence on _____ _____ . For example, Richard's most _____ tour is to Hobbiton because it has such a _____ set – even though most of the Hobbit houses _____ .

VOCABULARY

3 Go on a working holiday → SB 35

Complete the text about working holidays in New Zealand with these words. There are three extra words.

> dairy | destination | economy | establish | export product | generic | heritage | high standard of living | indeed | kiwi | nowadays | opportunities | offer | sector | unique | wool

New Zealand has a lot to _____ : fascinating landscapes, a _____ flora and fauna, a _____ , a casual lifestyle and its Maori _____ . In the past _____ was an important _____ and even _____ the agricultural _____ is essential to the country's _____ . So it's no surprise that a lot of the jobs that travellers do in New Zealand are _____ on farms; e.g. they work as a _____ farm assistant, or a _____ fruit picker. And because there aren't really many _____ where travellers can spend a lot of money on a farm, they will even be able to save some.

Revision A

→ Solutions p. 72

LANGUAGE

1 A holiday in New Zealand → SB 36; G1–4

In your exercise book, write an e-mail to your British friend Carmen about the holiday you and your family are going to go on. Be careful with tenses.

- tomorrow: taxi to airport
- flight to Auckland: 3 p.m.
- by this time tomorrow: sit on the plane
- weather in NZ: mostly sunny
- first day: visit Sky Tower

LANGUAGE

2 An interview with a film director → SB 39

Jenny (J), an Australian director, tells journalist Ahmed (A) about her new movie *Under Uluru*.
Use the right verb forms to make **conditional sentences type 1, 2 or 3** and complete the interview.

J: The plot is about some young Aboriginals who decide that if they _____

_____ (not fight) to keep their identity, they _____ (lose)

it. I think learning about Aboriginal culture is very important. Actually, if we _____

(not enter) our films in festivals like the Melbourne International Film Festival, a lot of people

_____ (not know) much about it.

A: What kind of film _____ (you / make) if you _____ (have) a big

Hollywood budget?

J: I don't think that's very likely! If you _____ (ask) me that question a few years ago,

I _____ (say) a big historical drama, but now I'm happy making

low-budget art films. I don't want to do anything else.

LANGUAGE

3 Mixed bag: Working on a cattle station → SB 39; G5, G7

Complete this text about a backpacker's experience on a cattle station in Australia.

Before I worked at the cattle station, I _____ as a waiter in Melbourne.

And if I _____ that flyer at my hostel, I _____

(never) the idea to work on a cattle station. The first weeks were _____ tough

because _____ work was _____ than expected. The boss _____ us go to work

before daylight! The _____ conditions were quite harsh, too. I always _____ a

hat to protect _____ from the sun. However, I enjoyed _____ around

the outback on horseback and I often stopped _____ at the _____

landscape. Actually, I wish I _____ there earlier.

Revision A

MEDIATION | **4** | **Camels in Australia?** → SB 41; S15

Deine indische Freundin Amrita benötigt für ihr Schulprojekt „Animals in Australia" noch Informationen. Nutze den folgenden Reisebericht und schreibe ihr eine E-Mail auf Englisch (ca. 200 Wörter), in der du ihr erklärst, wie die Kamele ins australische Outback gekommen sind, wieso sie zum Problem geworden sind und welchen Nutzen die Tiere heute haben.

Tip
Use different colours to mark the different pieces of information you want to include.

Von wegen Kängurus!

Seit Stunden durchqueren wir das australische Outback. Nicks Blick wischt am Horizont entlang wie ein Suchscheinwerfer. Über das Lenkrad hinweg hält er Ausschau nach Kamelen. „Letzte Woche waren hier ganz viele." Nick ist vor vier Jahren aus Adelaide heraufgezogen, weil er im Outback an Orte wollte, an die noch nie ein Weißer seinen Fuß gesetzt hat. „Da!" Nick bremst so abrupt, dass seine Rastazöpfe wippen. „Kamele!"

Immerhin ein halbes Dutzend. Ich hatte auf mehr gehofft. Denn mitten im Land der Koalas und Kängurus sollen Hunderttausende wilde Kamele leben. Die Zeitungen nennen sie eine „Plage". Ich stelle mir Horden von Tieren vor, die übers Land preschen, Staub aufwirbeln und dabei doch, in Australien, irgendwie fehl am Platz wirken müssen. Das wollte ich sehen.

Als Pioniere aus Europa im 19. Jahrhundert begannen, den Kern des australischen Kontinents zu erforschen, führten sie einhöckrige Kamele als Lastentiere ein – die ersten kamen aus Teneriffa, die meisten aus Pakistan und Indien. In wenigen Jahrzehnten wurden über 10.000 Dromedare ins Land gebracht, das letzte reiste 1907 ein. In den 1920er Jahren wurden die Dromedare von Autos und der Eisenbahn abgelöst. Viele Besitzer ließen ihre Tiere einfach frei. Sie dachten, die domestizierten Dromedare würden in der Wildnis bald verhungern. Stattdessen begannen sie sich zu vermehren. Zwischen 700.000 und eineinhalb Millionen wilder Kamele sollen es heute sein. Sie fressen kleineren Tieren die Blätter weg und verdrängen sie von den Wasserlöchern. Den Rinderfarmern trampeln sie die Zäune nieder, wenn sie auf der Suche nach Wasser in ihr Land eindringen. Alle drei bis vier Jahre lässt die Regierung Jäger in Flugzeugen ausziehen, um ein paar Zehntausend der Tiere zu erschießen.

Wir fahren weiter. Ohne Auto und Wasserflasche wäre man hier innerhalb weniger Stunden verloren. Kamele kommen hier gut zurecht, sie riechen Wasser kilometerweit. Da sie keine natürlichen Feinde haben, können sie ihre Population alle paar Jahre verdoppeln. Von einer „Plage" im Outback bemerke ich trotzdem nichts. Das Land scheint so unermesslich groß, dass es auch eine Million Kamele ohne Weiteres schluckt.

130 Kilometer vor Alice Springs halten wir an einer einfachen, lang gezogenen Holzbaracke. Wir setzen uns an einen Tisch hinter dem Haus. Nick bestellt Kamelburger. „Ooooh, sorry", säuselt die Bedienung. „Heute haben wir nur Kamelwürstchen." Die Würstchen sehen aus wie Merguez. Kamelfleisch ist dunkelrot, es schmeckt würzig, aber nicht nach Wild.

Am nächsten Morgen leuchtet die Halbwüste um Alice Springs in allen Rottönen. In der Nähe soll es eine Kamelfarm geben. Ich folge einer schmalen Piste und rumple ins Hinterland. Plötzlich entdecke ich in der Ferne eine kleine Karawane. Marcus Williams, der Chef der Farm, geht zu Fuß voran. Marcus nutzt seine Kamele nur für Ausritte mit Touristen. Tiere von anderen Farmen werden manchmal in die Arabischen Emirate exportiert. Dort sind sie als Rennkamele und auch als Fleischlieferanten sehr beliebt. In Australien gibt es nur ein halbes Dutzend Schlachthäuser, die überhaupt in der Lage sind, Kamele zu verarbeiten. „Nur darum sind sie zur Plage geworden", sagt Marcus. „Die Rindfleischlobby in Australien ist stark." Zähneknirschend habe sie zugelassen, dass die Regierung den Verzehr und Export von Kängurufleisch fördere. Aber sie wolle sich mit den Kamelen nicht selbst Konkurrenz machen.

Susann Sitzler, Zeit online, 12.06.2014

Revision A

5 Find the mistakes: Vietnamese immigrants → SB 41; G5, G7

Read the biographical profile of Mai, who escaped Vietnam by boat. Decide if the underlined words are correct or not. Correct the mistakes.

Mai Nguyen came to Australia with her mother when she (1) <u>had been</u> four. After (2) <u>the Vietnam War's end</u> in 1975, life in Vietnam was (3) <u>extreme difficult</u>. After Mai's grandfather (4) <u>has been arrested</u> by the new communist government, her mother (5) <u>decided taking</u> the chance and they left the country by boat. Many people (6) <u>who tried to leave</u> never made it out of the country and many died at sea. The boat that Mai and her mother left on was smaller and (7) <u>more crowded</u> than she (8) <u>had imagined herself</u>. Mai (9) <u>was most afraid</u> of (10) <u>attacking</u> by pirates. Like (11) <u>many other</u>, they ended up in a refugee camp in Malaysia. From there a lot of refugees (12) <u>were allowed to going</u> to countries like Australia, the US or France. But Mai and her mum (13) <u>wanted really</u> to go to Australia. If Mai's mother (14) <u>wasn't able to speak</u> English (15) <u>while she was being interviewed</u>, the Australian officials[1] (16) <u>might not had chosen</u> them. But Mai and her mother got the visa. Mai worked (17) <u>hardly</u> at school and at university and now (18) <u>she works</u> at (19) <u>the</u> IT company. Mai (20) <u>wasn't</u> back to Vietnam since then, but she (21) <u>will remember always</u> where she came from.

1 official [əˈfɪʃl] Beamte/-r

1. _____
_____
_____
_____
_____
_____
_____
_____
_____
_____
_____
_____

6 Mixed bag: Living in New Zealand → SB 41; G4–5

Complete Gabriel's personal statement about living in New Zealand.

I'm a true New Zealander and I _____ in Queenstown my whole life. _____ I love _____ about New Zealand is _____ breathtaking scenery. Even though I _____ to over twenty countries, I think the landscape of New Zealand is _____ beautiful than _____ other. Although I love _____ (explore) other countries, I prefer _____ (travel) around my _____ country now. There's so _____ to see: beaches, mountains, deserts and rainforests. If that _____ (not convince) you, _____ maybe New Zealand's rich indigenous culture will. For example, the national rugby team _____ the only team _____ a Maori haka before _____ match. _____, racism is still an issue here and people avoid _____ about it. But all in all, the people of New Zealand are some of _____ (friendly) people you _____ ever _____.

24 twenty-four

Text smart 1

Text analysis

READING

1 Different types of texts → SB 42; S6

a) *Decide if these characteristics belong to factual or fictional texts. Put them in the grid.*

> accurate facts and figures | creates suspense | factual report of events | gives information | narrative techniques | neutral style | provides entertainment | strong/dramatic language

factual texts	fictional texts

b) *Name at least two text types which match these purposes.*

1. Sharing your opinion on something you have experienced: _____

2. Teaching people how to do something step-by-step: _____

3. Providing information on the meaning of something: _____

READING

2 Parts of a text analysis → SB 42; S10

a) *Put the analysis of the book* The Fault in our Stars *by John Green in the correct order.*

☐ The book is written in a direct style. The two main characters are very honest with each other. This directness produces many moments of (dark) humour in their interactions. However, the characters often sound 'too' wise[1] and more like adults.

☐ The book aims to show that even if people have a deadly disease, their illness doesn't define who they are. Even though their death will cause pain for their loved ones, falling in love is still worth it: "you don't get to choose if you get hurt in this world, but you do have some say in who hurts you."

☐ All in all, the book clearly shows that the world "is not a wish-granting factory" and that pain is a necessary part of the human experience and therefore shouldn't be avoided. With all its ups and downs, the book is a roller coaster of emotions that hooks the reader.

☐ *The Fault in our Stars* can be described as a philosophical, bittersweet love story about two young cancer patients[2]. The novel has a first-person narrator and is told from the perspective of 16-year-old Hazel Lancaster, who is also the main character.

☐ *The Fault in our Stars* is a young adult novel which was written by John Green and published in 2012.

b) *Use the Reading skills box on p. 42 in your student's book and say which aspect of the analysis each part in a) is about.*

c) *Mark useful phrases that you can use for your own analyses.*

[1] wise [waɪz] weise [2] cancer patient ['kænsə 'peɪʃnt] Krebspatient/-in

Text smart 1

READING

3 Analysing a factual text → SB 43; S2, S4–5, S10

a) Read the article about lowering voting ages.

> **VOTES FOR TEENS: IS 16 THE NEW 18?**
> For some time now, people have been saying '50 is the new 40', '60 is the new 50' and even '60 is the new 40' … Around the world retirement ages are rising. In the UK, people tend to live ten years longer than they did in 1980. What has this got to do with lowering voting ages? It shows that what it means to be a particular age is changing.
>
> In almost all countries of the world the voting age is 18, and has been for a long time. In the UK, the voting age was lowered from 21 to 18 in 1969. Back then, 18-year-olds tended to have little experience of the world outside the area where they lived. Getting the latest news was difficult and they were mostly influenced by their parents' political views. Since then the quality of education has improved dramatically, and teenagers are very likely to have a much wider understanding of the world. Anyone with a smartphone can get the news around the clock, and many teenagers are very well-informed about politics. Research shows that parents' political views now have far less influence on teenagers than their friends' views.
>
> The main argument against lowering the voting age is that people younger than 18 are not able to make good-quality political decisions. However, in Austria and some states of Germany, where the voting age has been lowered to 16, there is no evidence that the quality of voting choices among the under 18-year-olds is any worse than that of older voters. The number of people who make poor-quality voting choices, such as voting or not voting for a party because of the leader's physical appearance, seems to be similar across all age groups.
>
> In a recent survey, 53 % of people in the UK said that the voting age should be lowered to 16. Unsurprisingly, the figure was highest among those aged 16 to 24 (70 %) and lowest among those over 65 (34 %). However, 53 % overall is still a majority. Perhaps it is time to say that, politically at least, '16 is the new 18'.
>
> Tori Whitnall, St Albo School student newspaper, September 2020

b) Use the context to guess the meaning of these words.

1. to lower
2. evidence
3. appearance

a) the way that sb or sth looks
b) to reduce something
c) sth that shows that something is true or false

c) Complete the first part of the analysis.

"Votes for teens" is an _____ that was published in a _____.

The _____ is Tori Whitnall, who _____ the article in _____.

The _____ of the article is to _____ people that the voting age should be 16.

The author presents facts and _____ about voting practices. She _____ voting now to voting in 1969 and gives strong _____ for lowering the voting age.

WRITING

d) Choose one word from each pair that describes best how the article is written. Use the words to write the next paragraph of your analysis (3–4 sentences) in your exercise book.

1. informal – formal
2. objective – convincing
3. examples – quotes
4. stories – statistics

e) Underline the most and least convincing argument in the text. Then write the third part of your analysis in your exercise book (2–3 sentences). Explain if the article fulfils its purpose.

26 twenty-six

Text smart 1

READING

4 A horrible discovery → SB 45; S2, S4–5, S10–11

a) *Charlie is a 13-year-old student who lives in a small town in Australia in the 1960s. One night Jasper Jones, the town's half-Aboriginal outcast[1], shares a horrible discovery with him. Read the text and do the exercises on the next page.*

Jasper Jones has come to my window. I don't know why, but he has. Maybe he is in trouble. Maybe he doesn't have anywhere else to go. Either way, he's just frightened the living shit out of me[2].

This is the hottest summer I can remember. It's near impossible to sleep, so I've spent most of my nights reading by the light of my kerosene lamp.

It's a full moon tonight, and very quiet. Neighbourhood dogs are probably too hot to bark their alarm. Jasper Jones is standing in the middle of our backyard. He shifts his feet from right to left. Jasper is tall. He's only a year older than me, but looks a lot more. He has a wiry body, but his shape and his muscles have already sorted themselves out.

Jasper Jones has outgrown his clothes. His shirt is dirty, and his short pants are just cut past the knee. He wears no shoes. He looks like an island castaway[3]. He takes a step towards me. I take one back.

"Okay. Are you ready?"

"What? Ready for what?"

"I tole you. I need your help, Charlie. Come on." His eyes are darting.

Charlie follows Jasper into the woods where Jasper shows him the dead body of Laura, his secret girlfriend. Jasper gives Charlie his word that he didn't kill her.

After a considerable silence, I turn to Jasper and let out a sigh. I speak quietly.

"Okay. What if I report it? Just me. Without you. What if I go to the police, or my parents, right now, and tell them what I've seen. I never mention your name. Ever."

Jasper Jones shakes his head. "Never work, Charlie. First off, why would you be here, all by yourself? Makes no sense."

"Jasper, there's still a chance that they won't blame you for this. Listen, we can still do this properly[4]. Tell the right people. The authorities. I mean, you're still protected by law, by …"

"Christ, Charlie! I ain't protected by shit. See, that's you bein afraid. You know that's not honest. You know what'll happen. This town, they think I'm a bloody[5] animal. They think I belong in a cage."

I look down and keep quiet.

"It's a big thing for me to trust you, Charlie. It's dangerous. And I'm asking you to do the same. I can't force you to do nuthin. But I hoped you might see things from my side. That's what you do, right? When you're readin. You're seeing what it's like for other people."

I nod.

"Well, Charlie, you think about this space here, and you think about what this means for me. And think about what I've got to do. What the right thing is."

I feel helplessly resigned. How could things be so messy and complex outside this quiet bubble of land in the woods?

"But Charlie, I mean, if you help me, nuthin is going to happen to you. I'll do everything it takes to keep you clear[6], orright? And that's a promise."

I nod again.

"You got to get brave, Charlie. It's all it is. I know you understand what I bin saying and why I'm in so much trouble. Me, I had to get brave in a hurry. Since I can remember, I had to do it all real quick, Charlie. Some days I feel so old, you know?"

"Yeah, I know it," I say.

"See, everyone here's afraid of something and nuthin. This town, that's how they live, and they don't even know it. They stick to what they know, what they bin told. They don't understand that it's just a choice you make."

I raise my head and look Jasper in the eye.

"I mean, I know people have always bin afraid of me. Kids specially, but old people too. They think I'm just half an animal with half a vote. That I'm no good. And I always used to think, why? They don't even know me. It never made sense. But then I realised, that's exactly why. That's all it is. It's so stupid, Charlie. But it means I don't hate them anymore."

From: Jasper Jones by Craig Silvey, adapted

---

1 outcast [aʊtkɑːst] Außenseiter/-in ○ **2** to frighten the living shit out of sb *vulg* [ˈfraɪtn ðə lɪvɪn ʃɪt aʊt əv ˈsʌmbədi] jmdn. zu Tode erschrecken ○ **3** castaway [ˈkɑːstəweɪ] Schiffbrüchige/-r ○ **4** properly [ˈprɒpli] richtig ○ **5** bloody *infml* [ˈblʌdi] verdammt *ugs.* ○
6 to keep sb clear [kiːp ˈsʌmbədi klɪə] jmdn. aus etwas raushalten

Text smart 1

b) *Find the words in the text for these definitions:*

1. thin but strong: _____
2. the people who make sure the law is followed: _____
3. opposite of hopeful: _____

c) *Use the context to guess the meaning of these words and match them with the definitions.*

1. to shift (l. 13)
2. to let out a sigh (l. 32)
3. to blame sb (l. 41)
4. to do sth properly (l. 42)
5. to stick to sth (l. 77)

a) to do sth the right way
b) to move from one position to another
c) to continue doing / believing sth
d) to say it's someone else's fault
e) to take a long and loud breath

d) *What are the themes of the excerpt? Choose the correct answers.*

1. ☐ racial issues
2. ☐ love
3. ☐ revenge
4. ☐ growing up
5. ☐ being an outsider
6. ☐ trust

e) *Answer these questions. Write notes.*

1. Why does Charlie want to go to the police? – _____

2. Why doesn't Jasper want to go to the police? – _____

3. Why does Jasper ask Charlie for help? – _____

f) *Explain these quotes. What do they tell you about Jasper and his hometown? Write in your exercise book.*

A
"This town, they think I'm a bloody animal. They think I belong in a cage." (ll. 46–47)

B
"Me, I had to get brave in a hurry. Since I can remember, I had to do it all real quick." (ll. 70–71)

C
"I mean, I know people have always been afraid of me. […] It's so stupid, Charlie. But it means I don't hate them anymore." (ll. 81–88)

g) *Analyse how the story is told. Write the answers to these questions in your exercise book. Include quotes.*

1. Describe the narrative perspective and its advantages and disadvantages.
2. Write a short characterisation of Jasper and Charlie. Compare the two characters.

Tip
Think of how the characters look | act | speak.

Across cultures 2

VOCABULARY

1 A sensitive situation → SB 49

a) *Complete the dialogue in which Owen says something insensitive. Put in the phrases in the correct form.*

> to be disrespectful | to have got a lot more in common with | to see beyond the stereotypes | to not mean to hurt sb's feelings | to offend | to see it from a different perspective

Emilia: I got another bad grade in my English test. I can't believe it.

Owen: No way! It was really easy. You must have learning difficulties.

Emilia: Don't say that, Owen! It _____ .

Owen: What did I say? Have I _____ you?

Emilia: Not really. But my brother has learning difficulties.

Owen: Oh, I'm sorry. I didn't know. I _____ .

Emilia: Unfortunately, people often make jokes about learning difficulties. But we _____ _____ people like my brother than you think.

Owen: What do you mean?

Emilia: Well, tell me something that you find really difficult.

Owen: Erm… Maths. I'm terrible at Maths. I try to understand it, but it's always really hard.

Emilia: Well, I think for my brother, almost everything is like that.

Owen: So you're saying that with people like your brother, I should try _____ _____ ?

Emilia: Exactly. Don't take this the wrong way, but I think you need to meet somebody with learning difficulties to help you _____ in your head.

b) *In your exercise book, make a mind map for the words 'tolerance' and 'respect'. Include words from the same word family, synonyms and antonyms. Use a dictionary or the internet for help.*

c) *Choose the right words to address the people in the photos respectfully. More than one can be correct.*

Coach   Doctor   Madam   Mr   Mrs   Professor   Sir

1   2   3   4   5

_____   _____   _____   _____   _____

twenty-nine **29**

2 Check-in Station 1

Unit 2 (Never) enough!

VOCABULARY

1 What can I do to help? → SB 51

○ Complete Aimee's article for her school magazine about teenagers and climate change.

Did you know that if everybody _____ living the way we do now, we would need 1.6 planets? And isn't it unfair that future _____ will have to _____ the mess we've left behind? That's why we need to _____ our carbon _____. We need to _____ the environment and stop _____ our natural resources. As a teenager, I thought there wasn't a lot I could do. But there are things that we teenagers can do. We can be the change that we want to see by having a more _____ lifestyle ourselves. And of course, we have the option of getting _____ in a _____ party or _____ against _____ change and _____ warming. We can and need to show that we care!

LISTENING

2 The five Rs of sustainability → SB 53; S12

A4 🔊 a) Listen to Aimee's podcast on sustainability and complete the text.

In the podcast Aimee talks about the five Rs of sustainability: refuse, _____, _____, _____ and _____, and how they are related to _____ we buy. According to her we don't only choose what _____ but also what _____ our choices have on _____.

b) Which of these points does Aimee make?

1. ☐ Refuse means buying less but better quality.
2. ☐ We should think about how many times we wear each piece of clothing.
3. ☐ It's easy to find out how to repair clothes.
4. ☐ Clothes can't be recycled as easily as other things.
5. ☐ Cheaply produced T-shirts have a higher carbon footprint.
6. ☐ Fast fashion may not be as cheap as it seems.

c) Name two things she suggests doing with unwanted clothes.

_____

_____

30 thirty

Station 1

3 Climate change and sports → SB 53; G9

*Aram read an article online about the impact of climate change on sports. Complete his comment with one pair of words in each sentence. Change them to participles with **-ed** or **-ing**.*

| alarm / convince | disappoint / scare | interest / bore | surprise / amaze | worry / tire |

I found this article about how climate change influences sports surprisingly _____, and I'm usually very _____ by scientific articles! I was _____ to read that climate change has an impact on sports that is truly _____ (and not in a positive way). It's very _____ that higher temperatures will make it harder for us to do sports outside and that athletes will feel _____ more quickly. It's _____ to see that even though there are _____ arguments to take action against climate change, the process is too slow. Reading about things like this makes me feel _____ and even a little _____ for the future.

4 The people making our clothes → SB 53; G9

Read this article about the working conditions in the fast fashion industry. Then underline the ten relative clauses and rewrite them with participles.

People who are employed in clothing factories can earn as little as $1 a day. Of course, most consumers would happily pay a little more to help workers who are trapped in poverty. The problem is an industry which is focused on keeping production costs as low as possible. In particular, some clothing companies that want to attract consumers with amazingly low prices can only do this thanks to employees who live and work in terrible conditions. Workers who are being exploited can be found in almost every industry, but the textile industry has become one of the best-known bad examples. However, there are fashion companies which are changing the industry. Also, consumers can make a difference by avoiding 'fast fashion' and by buying clothes that are being produced in a fairer and more sustainable way.

1. People _____

2   Station 1

LANGUAGE

5 An environmental fair at school → SB 53; G9

○ As a reporter for your school radio, you're
○ reporting live from the environmental fair
○ at your school. Use **participle constructions**
to describe the scene.
Add at least five more sentences.

I'm live at the environmental fair, where students can visit over 15 different stalls _informing about_ environmental issues. Right now, I'm standing at this year's most popular stall, which is a stall _____ fair trade food. _____

_____

_____

_____

_____

_____

LANGUAGE

6 A mental health youth activist → SB 54; G9

○ Find the right place for the clauses in this personal profile about a local teen mental health activist.
○ Then change the form to **participle constructions**.
○

> … because she knows … | … had posted … | … after she had written … | Although she was never … |
> As she had been upset about … | Before she became … | When she is asked …

_____ the way people talk about teenagers with mental health problems like depression or stress, 16-year-old Zora Jackson decided that it was time to do something about that. _____ very outgoing before, Zora now openly speaks out about mental health awareness. And _____ several articles for local newspapers and _____ content about the issue online, she became a state-wide spokesperson for the issue. _____ to speak about the mental health problems of young people, Zora always mentions the issues teenagers have to deal with on a daily basis, for example, the stress that social media can cause. _____ an activist, Zora had wanted to study architecture. However, now she wants to become a psychologist, _____ that this is where she will have a direct impact on people.

MEDIATION

7 Fridays for Future → SB 54; S15

Deine australische Freundin Kirra setzt sich für die Klimaschutzbewegung „Fridays for Future" in ihrem Ort ein. Sie möchte wissen, wie sich die Schülerinnen und Schüler in Deutschland organisieren, mit welchen Problemen sie konfrontiert sind und was sie für ihr späteres Leben mitnehmen können. Nutze den folgenden Artikel, um Kirra eine englische Mail (ca. 160 Wörter) zu schreiben, in der du ihre Fragen beantwortest.

Hinter den Kulissen von Fridays for Future

Letztens, als Klimaaktivisten dagegen demonstrierten, dass das Kohlekraftwerk Datteln 4 ans Netz geht, klingelt Luis' Handy. Er ist beim Familiengrillen, muss sich schnell entschuldigen, weil er, wie der Anrufer bettelt, „sofort eine Instagram-Story" fertig machen soll. Der Großvater war irritiert und hat die Dringlichkeit nicht verstanden. Doch im Grunde hat er in dieser Szene nur die fortschreitende Politisierung einer ganzen Schülergeneration am Beispiel seines Enkels beobachten können. Der Klimawandel bewegt diese Jugendlichen – und macht sie hartnäckig, konsequent und ziemlich professionell.

Luis (14) und seine Mitstreiterin Lilith (17) gehören zur Fridays-for-Future-Bewegung, die sich mit Streiks während der Schulzeit weltweit für effiziente und schnelle Klimaschutzmaßnahmen einsetzt. Die Fridaysbewegung in Berlin ist straff organisiert. An mehr als 100 Berliner Schulen gibt es Schülerdelegierte. Der Austausch findet über die sozialen Netzwerke statt. In Berlin wie anderswo sind die klimabewegten Schüler mit anderen Klima-Gruppen gut vernetzt, wie etwa „Extinction Rebellion", „Ende Gelände" oder dem Jugendrat der Generationen-Stiftung, der für einen Generationenrettungsschirm mobilisiert. Unterstützt wird Fridays for Future auch von zahlreichen Erwachsenengruppen wie den „Wissenschaftlern for Future".

Die Jugendlichen sind an den eigenen Schulen gut organisiert – das ist ihre Basis. Doch hat sich grundsätzlich etwas verändert. Während vor zehn Jahren die Klima- und Umwelt-AGs in den Schulen selbst von Schülern noch eher belächelt wurden und nicht besonders frequentiert waren, sind sie heute die kleinsten Einheiten, aus denen heraus für die großen Demos mobilisiert und organisiert wird. Die Schule hilft als Versammlungsort, hier sieht man sich, kann man reden. Auch mit aktiver Unterstützung der Klima- oder Umwelt-AGs an Schulen, aus denen viele Schülerdelegierte stammen, hat die Berliner Fridays-Truppe Arbeitsgruppen für viele Themen installiert: für politische Kommunikation, Pressearbeit, Social Media, Strukturen oder auch für die Essensversorgung auf Demonstrationen.

Der Aufwand neben der Schule ist hoch. Und in der Schule sind nicht alle begeistert. Ella (17) hat erlebt, wie irritiert Lehrer, Schüler und Eltern waren, als die Klimagruppe auf den Widerspruch aufmerksam machte, dass man einerseits zertifizierte Klimaschule sei, andererseits aber mit dem Flugzeug auf Klassenreise geht. Ella erinnert sich an Gespräche mit Mitschülern, Freunden, die entgeistert fragten: „Wollt ihr gar keinen Spaß?" Am Ende setzt sich die Klima-AG durch.

Die jungen Aktivisten haben vor allem gelernt, dass politisches Engagement und die dazugehörige Organisation harte Arbeit sind. Im ZDF sagte Clara Mayer (18): „Wir haben gelernt, Technik zu koordinieren, mit Politikern und Journalisten zu sprechen, formal korrekte Briefe zu schreiben und darin unsere Forderungen zu artikulieren." Gleichzeitig fragt Lilith sich öfter, ob sie noch die Noten schafft, die sie braucht, um später Jura zu studieren.

Die Geschichten, die Lilith, Luis und andere erzählen, zeugen von einer großen Verantwortlichkeit, die sie körperlich spüren und die sie dazu bringt, Regeln zu brechen und womöglich im nächsten Schritt auch zivilen Ungehorsam zu leisten. Viele dieser jungen Menschen sagen im Gespräch, dass sie eine Last tragen, die zu viele Erwachsene nicht tragen wollen, nämlich die der Überlebensfrage auf diesem Planeten.

Armin Lehmann, Der Tagesspiegel, 20.09.2020

2 Station 1

LANGUAGE

8 Find the mistakes: How much plastic do we need? → SB 55; G9

Read this article about the use of plastic. Decide if the underlined phrases are correct or not. Correct the mistakes.

'Responsible consumption and production' is part (1) <u>in</u> the United Nations 17 Sustainable Development Goals. However, this goal (2) <u>would be</u> hard to achieve if the world (3) <u>didn't</u> stop (4) <u>to use</u> so many plastic bags. In fact, one of (5) <u>the biggest</u> sources of single-use plastic (6) <u>are</u> supermarket plastic bags. ('Single-use plastic' means plastic things (7) <u>use</u> only once.)

In 2014, in the UK alone consumers (8) <u>have been using</u> more than (9) <u>7,6</u> billion bags, (10) <u>taking</u> home an average of 12 per person per month. Since (11) <u>paying</u> for bags was introduced, the number (12) <u>went down</u> by (13) <u>an amazingly</u> 95 %. The average British person now buys only four bags (14) <u>the year</u>.

Although (15) <u>being able to reduce</u> the use of plastic bags, the average UK home (16) <u>produces still</u> more than one ton of waste every year, and (17) <u>much</u> of that is plastic. It's clear that (18) <u>farer</u> steps to a more sustainable future (19) <u>need to be taken</u>.

1. _____

WRITING

9 Let's go dumpster diving[1]! → SB 55; S6-8

a) Put the parts in the correct order to make a letter to the editor of a newspaper. (Sometimes the letter contains the wrong register, but you will look at that in the next step.)

☐ Unfortunately, the article gave a very one-sided view of the topic. It presented dumpster diving as a fun activity to do with your friends to stop food waste and improve your ecological footprint.

☐ Another huge problem is that the genius who wrote this article forgot to mention that dumpster diving also comes with some dangers and I'm talking about from food that is not fresh anymore. Eating food from dumpsters can make people seriously ill.

☐ Having worked with homeless people for many years, I have seen dumpster diving being far from fun. On the contrary, for some people it is their only way of survival.

☐ Listen, I would like to point out that the article deals with an important topic and that I am not against dumpster diving at all. Actually, it is important to make more people aware of the fact that millions of tons of food are wasted yearly and that something has to be done about it.

☐ I am writing because I wanna complain about the article of May 17th, 'Let's go dumpster diving!'.

☐ However, it's not as trendy and fun as the author makes it sound.

☐ So, to tell the truth, the author should think more carefully before writing articles on complex topics like this. Therefore, I demand that he should at least add a short clarification at the end of the article.

b) Underline the words and phrases that are in the wrong register. Replace them with the more formal alternatives below and write the letter next to the line.

A To start with   **B** in response to   **C** writer of   **D** in particular   **E** suggest   **F** in my opinion

[1] dumpster diving [ˈdʌmpstə ˌdaɪvɪŋ] Containern *(weggeworfene Lebensmittel aus Abfallcontainern mitnehmen)*

Station 2

LISTENING

10 Fair trade → SB 57; S12

a) *Listen to a conversation in a supermarket about fair trade products. Then tick ✔ the correct speaker(s) for each statement.*

The speaker …	Jenny	Thomas
1. tries to buy only fair trade tea, coffee and chocolate.	☐	☐
2. thinks fair trade chocolate tastes better.	☐	☐
3. buys some coffee from small plantations.	☐	☐
4. often buys fruit and vegetables at the market.	☐	☐

b) *Listen again and complete the text.*

Jenny only has to pay _____ extra for the fair trade tea. Thomas isn't convinced that the money _____ the raw materials, but Jenny's sure that the amount helps parents to _____ _____ and to afford basic healthcare. You can easily find fair trade products if you _____. However, this supermarket isn't selling fair trade _____.

VOCABULARY

11 Fair trade: Facts and figures → SB 57

Complete the report about the impact fair trade has on workers. Use synonyms (=), opposites (↔) or other related words (→) for the words in blue.

Fair trade has helped to lift millions of people out of _____ (→ poor). Last year _____ (↔ less) than €150 million was paid as a 'fair trade premium' to producers in 74 countries by one of the _____ (→ to lead) fair trade organisations. That was money paid in addition to the price they could have got from other _____ (→ to buy). Over the last five years, people working as fair trade producers _____ (= to pay) 26% of the premium to provide _____ (→ to educate) for themselves and their families, and 31% on _____ (↔ to sell) equipment or improving their businesses in other ways. They have also spent it on _____ (↔ worse) food, healthcare and looking after _____ (↔ the young). _____ (= Nearly) 50% of fair trade plantation workers are female. Research shows that paying the premium directly to women is especially likely to _____ (= to make sth better) conditions in the wider community. Perhaps most important of all, fair trade organisations make a commitment to buy at fair prices in the _____ (↔ past), not just this year. This means that producers, their workers and the workers' families can _____ (= to prepare) for the future.

Station 2

LANGUAGE 12 Quality, not quantity → SB 57; G10

You are in a coffee shop buying a drink. A workshop is taking place and someone is explaining the differences between conventional and fair trade coffee plantations. Complete the talk with these pairs of verbs. Use **the present participle or infinitive after verbs of perception + object**.

feel / move	hear / cut	notice / pick
see / drink	see / smile	smell / burn down
watch / harvest	hear / chat / sing

"I _____ people _____ coffee in our shop every day. But how many of you really think about where coffee actually comes from? Imagine that you are at a typical large coffee plantation. The coffee beans are inside what we call 'the fruit'. You _____ the big, noisy harvesting machines _____ the fruit from the plants. These machines pick all the fruit, ready or not. It's very loud, and sometimes you can _____ the machines _____ the ground under your feet. The workers are badly paid and you don't _____ them _____ happily. You can _____ controlled fires _____ the nearby forest. The coffee company is also cutting down trees to grow more coffee plants. Now, let's compare that with a typical fair trade plantation. You _____ the workers _____ the coffee by hand. You _____ them _____ only the fruit which is ready. You _____ them _____ , and perhaps even _____ the latest pop songs together. Fair trade means that workers can be sure to get a good price for their coffee, so they can focus on quality instead of quantity."

LANGUAGE 13 130 million → SB 57; G11

Complete the online comment about a documentary film on the education of girls. Use the **present participle after verbs of rest and motion + object**.

catch / wonder	come out / feel
go / expect	go / feel	sit / not be able to
wake up / be	walk / look forward to

I _____ into the cinema _____ to find out a bit more about the daily lives of teenage girls around the world. And I did! I _____ in my chair _____ believe that there are about 130 million girls that aren't in school and aren't getting the education they should. I _____ of the film _____ very angry. Since seeing it, I _____ every morning _____ more thankful for my life. Because, unlike the girls in the film, I _____ to school _____ safe and welcomed, and I _____ home each afternoon _____ a warm dinner. I have often _____ myself _____ if the girls in the film were able to reach their goals and finish school.

Station 2

WRITING 14 Here, too? → SB 58; S7, S16

Write a short text (about 100 words) about the cartoon by Rina Piccolo and follow these steps.

1. Describe the cartoon.
2. Explain what the cartoon is making fun of.
3. Relate the cartoon to your own experience. Do you or your friends do the activity the cartoon makes fun of? Why / Why not? Give reasons.

LANGUAGE 15 How eco-friendly are e-scooters? → SB 58; G12

Complete this school magazine article about e-scooters with gerunds and infinitives.

> buy (2x) | drive | find | have (2x) | make | recycle | reduce (2x) | take | think | travel (2x) | use

A big part of climate action is _____ the CO_2 emissions of personal transport. So, in order _____ their carbon footprint, some of the students at Westside High School bought e-scooters. There are many reasons _____ around town on one of these instead of _____ or _____ public transportation. They're relatively cheap, you don't have to be worried about _____ a parking spot and you don't even need _____ a driver's license. They're also great for _____ to places where cars can't go. And of course, they use electric energy – ideally even green energy – instead of gas or diesel. Less pollution and fewer cars! But is it all good news? Unfortunately, no. It takes quite a lot of energy _____ an e-scooter. And often people buy one and then find out they don't enjoy _____ it as much as they thought they would. It's no use _____ lots of eco-friendly things at home if you only use them a few times. And this might not be the first thing you need _____ about when _____ a new e-scooter, but once it is broken, the batteries can be difficult _____ . So, if you're still thinking about _____ an e-scooter, borrow one from a friend for a few days first to try it out and ask the seller about recycling options.

2 Station 3

VOCABULARY **16 Word building** → SB 61

a) Write the preposition that can be added to all of the verbs in the centre of each mind map.

b) You've found a mobile on the street. It isn't locked. Write a story (about 150 words) about what happens next. Use as many verbs from one of the mind maps as possible.

WRITING **17 Don't watch the film without me!** → SB 62; G13–16

Alison visited her cousin Diego to watch a movie together. Underline the parts with indirect speech and then complete the picture story with the correct sentences in direct speech.

Last Sunday, Diego was on his phone when his cousin Alison came to visit. Diego was very focused on his screen and told Alison that she had come over just in time and that he was watching the new vampire movie that had been released the day before. Alison complained angrily that Diego should have waited for her and that he knew that she loved vampire movies. Diego felt a bit guilty because they had talked about watching the film together on Friday. He said he was sorry and admitted that he had already seen the first few minutes, but that they could watch it from the beginning and said that it would be more fun to watch it with her anyway. Then, Alison asked him if he really wanted to watch a whole movie on his phone. She told Diego that she had got a new tablet for her 16th birthday the week before and suggested that they could use it instead. Diego couldn't say no to that!

1

You've

2

3

4

Station 3

LANGUAGE 18 Screen time → SB 62; G13–15

Daisy is telling her friend Scarlett about a conversation with her younger brother, Ben, a few days ago. Put what Daisy and Ben said into **indirect speech**.

Daisy to Scarlett: On Saturday, my brother and I were sitting on the couch playing games on our phones when he suddenly asked me _____

_____. I realised that he might be right, so I suggested that _____.

Most phones record it automatically. He was surprised when he told me that _____

_____ and asked me _____

_____

_____. I was a bit embarrassed, but I had to admit that _____

_____

 and that _____

_____. Ben then said that

_____ and that

he _____

_____. I said that _____

_____.

> Ben: Do you think we spend too much time looking at screens?
>
> Daisy: We should check our screen time.
>
> Ben: *Oh wow!* I've already spent five hours on my phone today. How much time have you been on your phone? What have you been using it for?
>
> Daisy: *Oh dear...* I spent an average of seven hours a day on my phone this week. I was mostly using social media, but also playing games.
>
> Ben: We should put our phones away. I'm not going to look at my phone anymore today.
>
> Daisy: I'm not sure if I can do that, but I'll try.

SPEAKING 19 A survey on media usage → SB 62; S17

Look at the results from a school survey on media usage among students aged 13–18 in the UK. Talk about the results with a partner. What did you find surprising/obvious? How do these results relate to your own experience?

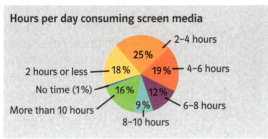

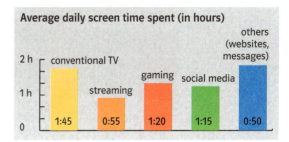

2 Station 3

LANGUAGE

20 Fake news → SB 62; G13–16

a) Read the conversation about fake news between a teenage brother and sister. Then draw lines to the verbs which would be best to report their statements.

1. Luca: The reason I like this website is because it has weird, crazy news!
2. Jess: Don't look at silly websites with fake news.
3. Luca: You're always telling me what to do!
4. Jess: Fake news can be dangerous, especially if lots of people repost it.
5. Luca: OK, I won't repost any fake news.
6. Jess: A lot of people repost fake news without realising it.
7. Luca: You reposted a crazy story about a dog that can speak, remember?
8. Jess: The story came from a serious news website.

`advise`
`complain`
`point out`
`explain`
`promise`
`remind`
`inform`
`warn`

b) Use the verbs you chose in a) to report what Luca and Jess said. Write in your exercise book.

WRITING

21 Not in my backyard! → SB 63; S6–8

As a local news reporter, you have to write an article about a controversial project in your village. Write about 160 words in your exercise book following these instructions:

1. Use the information below to write an outline for your article. Think of possible pros and cons that could be mentioned at the meeting.
2. Then write your article and include what the people at the meeting said. You can use quotes, indirect speech or just sum up the given arguments.

> **Useful phrases**
>
> Most / Many / Some / A few people thought / felt / agreed / argued that … | Mr / Mrs … / a resident / the mayor made the point / mentioned that …

Situation:
- new project: plans to build a wind farm with ten wind turbines in a field near the village
- town hall meeting[1] last Monday to discuss the pros and cons of the project

Opinions expressed during the meeting:

Raven Swanson (company representative[2] of Vector Wind Inc.): Wind energy is one of the cleanest forms of energy.

Gracy-May Leach (activist): The noise of the wind turbines can affect animals. Birds could even get killed. What will happen to the protected bird species that nests nearby?

Archer Watt (mayor): A wind farm would create jobs in the region and provide an extra income for landowners.

Gabriella Dolan (farmer): Even though the money I would be able to make by renting out my land would be nice; I think the protection of our beautiful countryside is more important.

Shakil Fenton (activist): We must make the move towards more renewable sources of energy! They provide clean and low-cost energy. Climate change is happening now.

Saif Roach (resident): This isn't a good place for a wind farm. It's too close to the village. I'm worried about noise pollution.

[1] town hall meeting [ˌtaʊn ˈhɔːl ˌmiːtɪŋ] Bürgerversammlung   [2] company representative [ˌkʌmpəni ˌreprɪˈzentətɪv] Firmenvertreter/-in

Green Line 5

Workbook

Word banks

Bayern

Word bank

Typical Aussie

Dangerous and poisonous animals

brown snake

box jellyfish

dingo

redback spider

saltwater crocodile (saltie)

More animals

kangaroo

thorny dragon

koala

wombat

Tasmanian devil

emu
[ˈiːmjuː]

kookaburra
[ˈkʊkəˌbʌrə]

wallaby
[ˈwɒləbi]

platypus
[ˈplætɪpəs]

goanna
[ɡəʊˈænə]

Sports

cricket

rugby

tennis

soccer

touring car racing

Foods

Chicken Parma
(with parmesan cheese)

Anzac Biscuits
(oatmeal cookies)

Pavlova
(a berry cake)

Witchetty Grub
(worms on toast)

Lamington
(jam-filled cake with coconut)

Word bank

Australia – country of contrasts

outback / bush   beach / coastline

farmland / rural area   metropolis / urban area

rainforest   mining

indigenous / Aboriginal culture   Western culture

Emergencies and first aid

Where are you?	What could happen?	First aid
in the wilderness 	to get sunburned / sunburnt to get bitten by a snake to be poisoned by a spider to be dehydrated [diːhaɪˈdreɪtɪd] to break one's arm / leg to be stung by an insect / a bee	to apply ointment to need medication to make an emergency call to call an ambulance to call the air ambulance to call Triple Zero (Australia) / 999 (UK) / 911 (USA)
at the beach 	to have a swelling to pass out / to faint [ˈfeɪnt] to feel out of breath to be stung by a jellyfish to drown	to put on a bandage to have sb lie down to take a pulse to get help from a lifeguard to do mouth-to-mouth resuscitation [ˈmaʊθ tʊ ˈmaʊθ rɪsʌsɪˈteɪʃən]
in the city 	to have an accident to have an infection to have food poisoning to have a fever / headache to have a fracture / sprained ankle [ˈspreɪnd ˈæŋkl]	to visit a doctor to get medication to take a tablet to be in hospital

3

Word bank

A country profile

Geography

continent
area
border
capital
region
country
landscape

Population

community
society
indigenous people
citizen / inhabitant
ethnicity
migration

Economy

company
trade
goods
resources
labour
capital
financial / agricultural / … sector

Language

speaker
minority language
dialect
accent

History

(civil) war
peace
colonisation
independence
(ancient) [ˈeɪnʃənt] civilisation
empire
era / period

Culture

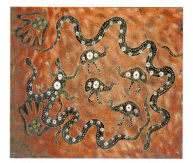

beliefs
values
traditions
religion
cuisine [kwɪˈziːn] / food
arts
social habits
holidays
customs
music

Government

democracy
chancellor
prime minister
president
monarchy
king / queen
republic
dictatorship
election

Word bank

Identity

Interests

to be into music / dance / art / ...
to be a cyclist / blogger / ...
to be a fashionista / foodie / ...
to love partying / swimming / ...

Gender / sexual orientation

to be part of the LGBTQIA+ community
to be transgender / non-binary / ...
to be homosexual / gay / lesbian / bisexual / ...

Appearance

to dye your hair pink / blue / ...
to dress as a goth / metalhead / ...
to have piercings
to have tattoos

Disabilities

to have a (learning) disability
to use a wheelchair
to be deaf / hard-of-hearing
to wear a hearing aid
to be blind / partially sighted
to have a visual impairment
to live in an accessible [əkˈsesəbl] home
to live with a mental illness

Religion

to wear a veil / cross / hijab / niqab / burka
to pray / worship
to believe in
to be a Buddhist / Christian / Jew / Muslim / Sikh / ...
to be an atheist [ˈeɪθiːɪst]
to go to church / the temple / the synagogue [ˈsɪnəɡɒɡ] / the mosque
to eat kosher / halal
to fast

Reacting politely / sensitively

Perhaps I didn't make myself clear.
Could we address this problem?
I was wondering if ...
I don't mean to trouble / offend you, but ...
Sorry for interrupting, but may I ask why ...?
Correct me if I'm wrong. I believe ...

I don't think it's fair / acceptable to ...
Could you please show more respect for ...?
It's hard to judge if you don't know ...
There are different ways to live one's life, don't you think?
I apologise if it offends you to see / hear ...
Maybe I shouldn't have mentioned ...
I'm glad you mentioned ...
I'm sorry but I need to ask you to ...
Do you think it's appropriate to ... ?
This may be a misunderstanding.
The message I want to get across is ...
I hope it doesn't bother you that ...
As far as I know ...
Would you mind (+ -ing) ...?
Hold on a second. I'm not so sure ...
Excuse me. I would like ...

Word bank

Talking about climate change

Causes

increase in greenhouse gases
exploiting resources
deforestation [diːˌfɒrɪˈsteɪʃn]
destruction of ecosystems
population increase
using fossil fuels
water / air pollution

Effects

global warming
rising temperature
rising sea level
higher ocean temperature
increase in heavier rain
melting glaciers / permafrost
heat risks
extinction / migration of species

food
- to write a grocery list
- to go to the local farmer's market
- to eat less meat
- to start composting [ˈkɒmpɒstɪŋ]
- to buy fresh and local food

consumption
- to buy second-hand
- to use recycled paper
- to reject junk mail
- to fix things

plastic
- to use a reusable water bottle
- to not use straws
- to bring your own bags
- to say no to single-use plastic
- to use biodegradable [ˌbaɪəʊdɪˈɡreɪdəbl] materials

What can I do?

transportation
- to use public transport
- to drive less
- to carpool
- to cycle

home
- to choose energy efficient devices
- to turn off devices when you don't use them
- to use a clothesline
- to use LED light bulbs [ˈbʌlb]
- to switch to green power

activism
- to vote in elections
- to learn more about climate change
- to protest / to strike
- to encourage friends to become active
- to plant trees
- to sign petitions
- to do a beach clean-up

6

Word bank

The ABCs of activism

A activist

B banner

C council

D digital activism

E equality

F fundraiser [ˈfʌndreɪzə]

G global warming

H human rights

I impact

J justice

K keep trying

L laws

M movement

N non-violent

O organised

P petition

Q quit flying

R research information online

S strike

T teach others

U unsatisfied citizens

V volunteer

W women's rights

X xenophobia [zenəˈfəʊbɪə]

Y youth activism

Z zero waste

Word bank

Discussion

Useful phrases for the moderator

Introduction

- Welcome to our debate on the topic of ...
- The question we are discussing today is ...
- I'd like to introduce ..., who is ...

Conclusion

- Time is almost up now.
- Could you summarise your ideas, please?
- Our discussion has shown that ...
- Thank you for your participation.

Keeping order

- Can we please stay with ... for the moment?
- Would you please come to the point?
- Mr / Ms ..., what is your opinion of ...?
- Would you please listen to ...?
- If I may stop you there – ... would like to comment.
- Mr / Ms ..., would you like to reply to this?
- It will be your turn in a minute.

Useful phrases for participants

Stating your arguments

- To start with, ...
- There are three points I would like to make.
- I'm of the opinion that ...
- I'm sure that ...
- Let me give you an example.
- Statistics / Surveys show that ...
- It's also important to know ...
- I would like to add that ...
- We should talk about what this means for ...
- Let me repeat what I said earlier.

Defending your arguments

- I see your point, but ...
- That's not quite what I meant by ...
- I would suggest / recommend ...
- On the one hand ..., (but) on the other hand ...
- That is certainly true, but at the same time ...
- What I'm trying to say is ...
- Even if that is so ...
- I agree in principle, but ...
- What I actually said was ...
- This implies that ...

Interacting with other participants

- I would like to comment on what was said about ...
- As we have just heard from ...
- Excuse me, could you explain that again, please?
- Sorry, can I just make a point?
- I completely disagree with you on ...
- I would question that argument.
- I think you have misunderstood something.
- I'm not sure it is as simple as that.
- What is your position on ...?
- I fully agree with / support your view.
- I think you're right to a point.

Word bank

Structuring argumentative texts

Introduction

– Today, you can see … everywhere.
– Obviously, most people …
– The question of the essay is whether …
– In this text, I would like to address …
– The issue focused on is …
– My goal is to …
– As the following arguments will show, …

(Counter) Arguments

– First (of all), …
– The main reason is …
– Second / Third / Next, …
– However / Nevertheless, …
– On the one hand …, on the other hand …
– As a result, / Therefore …
– Although it is true that …, it would be wrong to claim that …
– Some might say … / One could argue that …
– (But) I am convinced that …
– Furthermore / Additionally / In addition, …
– Moreover / Also, …
– Another aspect / point is that …

Quotations / Facts

– The numbers show …
– According to …,
– An important fact is …
– Therefore …
– As … have / has often said, …
– It is a fact that …
– For several reasons, it is necessary …
– There are many / various reasons for this.
– Another significant point is …
– Because of … / That is why …
– For example / instance, … / Look at …

Conclusion

– To sum up … / In conclusion, …
– In summary, it can be said that …
– In my opinion, …
– My suggestion would be …
– After all, …
– Weighing the pros and cons, I conclude / come to the conclusion that …
– All in all I believe that …

Synonyms of common words

good	bad	interesting	to say
great	poor	exciting	to argue
fabulous	awful	fascinating	to state
fine	disgusting	amazing	to describe
acceptable	unacceptable	entertaining	to claim
wonderful	inappropriate	impressive	to disagree
perfect	brutal [ˈbruːtl]	provocative [prəˈvɒkətɪv]	to note
fantastic	worrying	surprising	to suggest
excellent	horrible	unusual	to mention
neat	terrible	refreshing	to explain
great idea	unacceptable risk	interesting question	to describe the chart
good example	inappropriate behaviour	surprising fact	to suggest an idea
acceptable solution	poor conditions	impressive work	to mention a need to
excellent way	terrible damage	unusual point	to state the obvious

Word bank

Applications and jobs

talking about work

out of work
to lose one's job
to be unemployed
to get fired
to change careers
to retire

looking for work
to apply for / to
to go job-hunting
to find a job
to send in an application
to be invited to / to have an interview
to search for a job

finding work
to hire sb
to employ sb
to offer sb a job
to look for a candidate
to be successful

in work
to work for a company
to be a teacher / chef / manager / electrician
to work the night shift
to have a full-time / part-time job
to be employed
to have colleagues [ˈkɒliːg] / co-workers
to be self-employed

False friends

to get a **promotion** – befördert werden	≠	promovieren – **to do one's doctorate** [ˈdɒktərət]
to be given **notice** – eine Kündigung erhalten	≠	eine Notiz schreiben – **to write a note**
to **resign** / to **quit** – kündigen	≠	resignieren – **to give up**
to get a **pension** – Rente beziehen	≠	in einer Pension übernachten – **to stay at a B&B** / **guesthouse**
chef – Koch	≠	Chef – **boss**
biro [baɪrəʊ] – Kugelschreiber	≠	Büro – **office** / **bureau** [ˈbjʊərəʊ]
résumé (AE) / **CV (BE)** – Lebenslauf	≠	Resümee, Zusammenfassung – **summary**

Word bank

Around school – AE vs. BE

American English	British English
stand in line	queue

American English	British English
principal	head teacher

janitor	caretaker

period	lesson

schedule	timetable

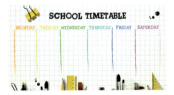

restroom / bathroom	toilet / loo *infml*

report card	report

American English	British English
transportation	transport

soccer	football

8th-grader	a Year 8 pupil

garbage / trash	rubbish

Math	Maths

grade	mark

high school diploma	GCSE / A Levels

Bildquellennachweis

1.1 F1online digitale Bildagentur, Frankfurt (Marco Govel/Westend61); **1.2** ShutterStock.com RF, New York (Yunsun_Kim); **2.1** ShutterStock.com RF, New York (Ken Griffiths); **2.2** ShutterStock.com RF, New York (Dewald Kirsten); **2.3** Thinkstock, München (iStockphoto); **2.4** ShutterStock.com RF, New York (Peter Yeeles); **2.5** Picture-Alliance, Frankfurt/M. (Jack Green/OKAPIA); **2.6** Thinkstock, München (JohnCarnemolla); **2.7** iStockphoto, Calgary, Alberta (JohnCarnemolla); **2.8** iStockphoto, Calgary, Alberta (eeqmcc); **2.9** Getty Images, München (David & Micha Sheldon); **2.10** Getty Images Plus, München (CraigRJD); **2.11** ShutterStock.com RF, New York (colacat); **2.12** stock.adobe.com, Dublin (bertys30); **2.13** ShutterStock.com RF, New York (AustralianCamera); **2.14** Okapia, Frankfurt (Alan Root); **2.15** ShutterStock.com RF, New York (Little Adventures); **2.16** Getty Images Plus, München (Kolbz); **2.17** dreamstime.com, Brentwood, TN (Zuperpups); **2.18** ShutterStock.com RF, New York (Neale Cousland); **2.19** ShutterStock.com RF, New York (Tungphoto); **2.20** Picture-Alliance, Frankfurt/M. (ASA / Thomas Urner); **2.21** ShutterStock.com RF, New York (Toong); **2.22** ShutterStock.com RF, New York (NoirChocolate); **2.23** ShutterStock.com RF, New York (Volha Zvonik); **2.24** ShutterStock.com RF, New York (nicemyphoto); **2.25** ShutterStock.com RF, New York (nelea33); **3.1** iStockphoto, Calgary, Alberta (Kptan123); **3.2** Alamy stock photo, Abingdon (Outback Australia); **3.3** Interfoto, München (David Wall); **3.4** Getty Images Plus, München (Xin He DigitalVision); **3.5** Alamy stock photo, Abingdon (Raymond Warren); **3.6** ShutterStock.com RF, New York (THPStock); **3.7** Bridgemanimages.com, Berlin (Richard Bryant/Arcaid); **3.8** ShutterStock.com RF, New York (ChameleonsEye); **3.9** stock.adobe.com, Dublin (vekidd); **3.10** ShutterStock.com RF, New York (myphotobank.com.au); **3.11** Alamy stock photo, Abingdon (redbrickstock.com/Ian Waldie); **4.1** F1online digitale Bildagentur, Frankfurt (Image Source); **4.2** MEV Verlag GmbH, Augsburg (MEV, Augsburg); **4.3** ShutterStock.com RF, New York (Tim Roberts Photography); **4.4** stock.adobe.com, Dublin (aaabbc); **4.5** stock.adobe.com, Dublin (Okea); **4.6** Picture-Alliance, Frankfurt/M. (united archives/Franken); **4.7** iStockphoto, Calgary, Alberta (oversnap); **5.1** iStockphoto, Calgary, Alberta (gchutka); **5.2** iStockphoto, Calgary, Alberta (SoumenNath); **5.3** Getty Images Plus, München (nautiluz56); **5.4** iStockphoto, Calgary, Alberta (filrom); **5.5** ShutterStock.com RF, New York (Brian A Jackson); **5.6** ShutterStock.com RF, New York (Motortion Films); **6.1** ShutterStock.com RF, New York (Rich Carey); **6.2** ShutterStock.com RF, New York (Piyaset); **6.3** stock.adobe.com, Dublin (monticellllo); **6.4** ShutterStock.com RF, New York (HollyHarry); **6.5** stock.adobe.com, Dublin (contrastwerkstatt); **6.6** 123rf Germany, c/o Inmagine GmbH, Nidderau (Olena Yakobchuk); **6.7** Avenue Images GmbH, Hamburg (PhotoDisc); **6.8** Getty Images Plus, München (Halfpoint); **7.1** ShutterStock.com RF, New York (MikeDotta); **7.2** ShutterStock.com RF, New York (nicostock); **7.3** stock.adobe.com, Dublin (JackF); **7.4** ShutterStock.com RF, New York (goodluz); **7.5** Getty Images Plus, München (Photodisc/D-BASE); **7.6** stock.adobe.com, Dublin (Africa Studio); **7.7** stock.adobe.com, Dublin (Lasse Kristensen); **7.8** Getty Images, München (PATRICK HERTZOG / AFP); **7.9** ShutterStock.com RF, New York (marekuliasz); **7.10** stock.adobe.com, Dublin (gorosi); **7.11** ShutterStock.com RF, New York (Allison C Bailey); **7.12** ShutterStock.com RF, New York (wavebreakmedia); **7.13** dreamstime.com, Brentwood, TN (Ericcrama); **7.14** VISUM Foto GmbH, München (Alfred Buellesbach); **7.15** ShutterStock.com RF, New York (REDPIXEL.PL); **7.16** stock.adobe.com, Dublin (Wrangler); **7.17** ShutterStock.com RF, New York (Martin Wheeler III); **7.18** iStockphoto, Calgary, Alberta (Anna Bryukhanova); **7.19** Picture-Alliance, Frankfurt/M. (SULUPRESS.DE); **7.20** ShutterStock.com RF, New York (Monkey Business Images); **7.21** ShutterStock.com RF, New York (Aaron Amat); **7.22** Getty Images Plus, München (SDI Productions); **7.23** ShutterStock.com RF, New York (Hans Christiansson); **7.24** Action Press GmbH, Hamburg (GAUL,HANS-GEORG); **7.25** ShutterStock.com RF, New York (Michal Urbanek); **7.26** Okapia, Frankfurt (Berthold Singler); **8.1** Getty Images Plus, München (Wavebreakmedia); **8.2** stock.adobe.com, Dublin (pressmaster); **8.3** iStockphoto, Calgary, Alberta (Mark Bowden); **9.1** ShutterStock.com RF, New York (Carboxylase); **9.2** ShutterStock.com RF, New York (Carboxylase); **9.3** ShutterStock.com RF, New York (Carboxylase); **9.4** ShutterStock.com RF, New York (Carboxylase); **10.1** stock.adobe.com, Dublin (merfin); **10.2** stock.adobe.com, Dublin (merfin); **10.3** stock.adobe.com, Dublin (merfin); **10.4** stock.adobe.com, Dublin (merfin); **10.5** stock.adobe.com, Dublin (merfin); **10.6** stock.adobe.com, Dublin (merfin); **10.7** stock.adobe.com, Dublin (merfin); **10.8** stock.adobe.com, Dublin (merfin); **10.9** stock.adobe.com, Dublin (merfin); **10.10** stock.adobe.com, Dublin (merfin); **10.11** stock.adobe.com, Dublin (merfin); **10.12** stock.adobe.com, Dublin (merfin); **10.14** stock.adobe.com, Dublin (merfin); **10.15** stock.adobe.com, Dublin (merfin); **10.15** stock.adobe.com, Dublin (merfin); **11.1** Avenue Images GmbH, Hamburg (image 100); **11.2** iStockphoto, Calgary, Alberta (Lorraine Boogich); **11.3** Getty Images Plus, München (E+/fstop123); **11.4** Getty Images Plus, München (E+/skynesher); **11.5** stock.adobe.com, Dublin (D. Ott); **11.6** Thinkstock, München (iStockphoto); **11.7** Alamy stock photo, Abingdon (MBI); **11.8** iStockphoto, Calgary, Alberta (Juanmonino); **11.9** stock.adobe.com, Dublin (Ivan Kopylov); **11.10** Thinkstock, München (Hemera); **11.11** Picture-Alliance, Frankfurt/M. (Jörg Carstensen); **11.12** Avenue Images GmbH, Hamburg (StockDisc); **11.13** Avenue Images GmbH, Hamburg (StockDisc); **11.14** Getty Images Plus, München (kali9/E+)

Station 3

LISTENING **22**   **Behind the wheel** → SB 63; S12

A 6

a) *Danez is visiting his new friend Melissa. Together with Melissa's dad, Mr Kent, they're sitting at the breakfast table. Listen to their discussion about driving and say which statement describes Danez's **(D)**, Melissa's **(M)** and Mr Kent's **(K)** opinion best. There is one extra statement.*

1. ☐ The car as people's main means of transport is a thing of the past.
2. ☐ We need to change to electric cars as soon as possible.
3. ☐ Without cars, we wouldn't be able to do a lot of things.
4. ☐ To be able to drive a car is an important skill in life.

b) *Listen again. Are these statements true or false? Tick ✔ the correct answer and correct the wrong statements.*

	true	false
1. Danez uses public transport or his skateboard to get around London. Correction: _____	☐	☐
2. Danez admits that public transport is too expensive. Correction: _____	☐	☐
3. According to Danez, next to petrol[1], the costs for a car also include buying the car, insurance[2] and cleaning. Correction: _____	☐	☐

c) *Listen again and answer the questions. Take notes.*

1. Next to the costs, what are the other two main problems with public transport in rural areas according to Melissa? _____

2. What were the things that Melissa worried about before getting her licence?
_____

d) *Tick ✔ the statements mentioned about cars and the environment.*

1. ☐ People in rural areas often carpool because it's better for the planet.
2. ☐ Because a lot of teenagers know that cars affect the environment negatively, they don't consider them as cool anymore.
3. ☐ Especially in big cities with a lot of traffic, air pollution is a big issue.
4. ☐ A person's carbon footprint increases significantly when they own a car.
5. ☐ Electric cars aren't very eco-friendly if they use electricity from fossil fuels.

e) *Underline the correct answer.*

1. After school, Melissa is planning to   move to the city. | travel abroad. | buy a car.
2. In the end, Danez admits that having a car can sometimes be   exciting. | useful. | motivating.

1 petrol ['pətrl] Benzin   **2** insurance [ɪnˈʃʊərns] Versicherung

2 Skills Story

SKILLS 23 Teens and opinions → SB 64; S8

a) *Read part of a discussion from a classroom debate about energy solutions. The students sometimes don't use the right register. Look at the marked phrases and use different colours to mark the ones that are **suitable** or **rude**. Then replace the rude phrases with more formal alternatives.*

> Host: (1) **Let's return to our original question.** Alfie, you believe that more nuclear power stations should be built.
> Alfie: Yes, I do. (2) **I'm not saying that** we shouldn't develop renewable energy too, of course, but we need nuclear …
> Tia: (3) **Are you being serious right now?**
> Host: (4) **Be quiet and let him finish.**
> Alfie: … we need nuclear power as part of our energy mix.
> Host: (5) **Now you can speak, Tia.**
> Tia: The dangers of nuclear power can't be ignored!
> Alfie: (6) **What exactly do you mean by 'dangers'?**
> Tia: Past accidents at nuclear power stations have shown that no matter how safe we think they are, accidents did and will happen. Renewable energy can supply …
> Alfie: (7) **Stop!** What happens when there isn't any?
> Tia: (8) **I'm not sure I follow you.**
> Alfie: Renewable energy sources are a lot more unreliable. What happens when there isn't any sunshine or wind?
> Tia: We can store renewable energy in batteries which …
> Alfie: (9) **That's nonsense!**
> Host: (10) **Let's give Tia a chance to explain.**

_____
_____
_____
_____
_____
_____
_____
_____
_____
_____

b) *In a discussion the host often reformulates arguments to make something the participant said clearer. Read more of the arguments that Alfie makes and match the sentences with the reformulations.*

1. Unlike traditional fossil fuels, nuclear power doesn't produce CO_2 emissions.
2. I take Tia's point about disasters in the past, but those mostly affected old nuclear power stations. The new ones are much safer. We can't wait until all electricity comes from renewable sources.
3. Technology is developing fast. Modern nuclear power stations are completely different to ones built in the 1950s and 1960s.
4. Of course, it is important to discuss what we do with nuclear waste, but there is actually very little waste created.

☐ Do you mean another serious nuclear disaster is less likely with modern nuclear power plants?

☐ So, if I understand you correctly, nuclear energy is better for the environment than we think.

☐ Are you telling us that there is zero risk from nuclear waste?

☐ So, what you're also saying is that we need to speed up the process of changing to more renewable energy sources.

VOCABULARY 24 Organising vocabulary → SB 69

a) *In your exercise book, make a grid with these headings:*
climate and weather | state of emergency | describing bad behaviour.
Then put the words into the correct group and add at least three words of your own to each group.

> access | annoying | blackout | disgusting | drizzle | drought | evil |
> to freeze | pathetic | ration | reduction | riot

b) *Imagine there is a blackout. Use some of the words from a) to write four short social media posts (each no longer than 140 letters) about what happened and how people react to the situation differently.*

READING 25 We need to stand up for nature → SB 69; S2, S4–8

a) *Read the article and do the exercises on the following page.*

Meet generation Greta: young climate activists around the world

Dylan D'Haeze, 16, Washington State, US: This autumn, Dylan releases the fourth environmental documentary in his award-winning series, *Kids Can Save The Planet*. "Film-making empowers[1] me because I can visually show problems and solutions in a way that is much easier to understand," says Dylan, who directs, narrates and films his documentaries. It was ocean pollution that first struck him when he travelled through California three years ago: "The plastic waste we saw on beaches really scared me, and my mum suggested that instead of being afraid, I could do something about it," says Dylan, who is home-schooled by his parents, Dawn and Kevin, both film-makers. "At first I felt helpless, but then I started discovering solutions that were actually really simple, like eating with bamboo cutlery and using beeswax wrap instead of clingfilm," he says.

Dylan and Dawn are now planning the ultimate road trip. For six months, they will drive an electric car from their home on the west coast across America to Washington DC, filming as they go. Dylan will interview leaders of green initiatives, youth activists from the nationwide *Sunrise Movement* and pioneers developing renewable energy. As he travels, he will present his latest film in high schools and colleges, and speak in city halls[2] and state capitals, asking people to make, on camera, a commitment to positive change. According to Dylan, the main problem is trying to convince the government and big companies that climate change is a serious problem.

Yola Mgogwana, 11, Cape Town, South Africa: "I see the effects of climate change every single day," says Yola, from her home in Khayelitsha, one of Cape Town's impoverished townships[3]. "Our weather is not normal – one day it is hot, the next day it's raining heavily. It's a huge problem for farmers, and mudslides wash away houses." Eighteen months ago, Cape Town experienced its most severe drought in a century. Residents' water consumption was limited to 50 litres a day and the city was just weeks away from "day zero", when taps would run dry. "For me, that was a big sign that we need to stand up for nature," she says.

In January, Yola began volunteering with the *Earthchild Project* which integrates environmental education into classrooms and communities. "Our mission is to monitor our school's food, water and electricity usage, and encourage other learners to reduce their consumption." The school's organic vegetable garden helps feed pupils[4], and a worm farm transforms food waste into compost. "Climate change is a foreign topic to my family – without this club I would be in the dark," says Yola, who takes inspiration from the Zulu word "ubuntu", meaning "I am because you are."

In March, Yola spoke in front of 2,000 young people in Cape Town, and she presents talks at neighbouring schools. "I want to show the world that we, as black youth from Cape Town's poor communities and townships, do care about the climate – because we are the ones that get affected the most." She wants the South African government to take action. "The crisis is now. People are dying."

Lilly Platt, 11, Zeist, the Netherlands: As Lilly walks to and from school, she litter-picks, often collecting up to 400 pieces of rubbish. She started four years ago, shortly after she and her family moved to the Netherlands from London. She was learning to count in Dutch with her grandfather and as they walked, they counted 91 pieces of litter within just 15 minutes. "My grandpa told me how plastic on the ground eventually makes its way to the ocean," she says, "so I decided I had to do something about it. We picked it all up and took a photo to post on social media." After that first pick-up, Lilly started researching plastic pollution and was horrified to read about the oceans' "microplastic soup".

"Plastic pollution just shows that we consume too much," Lilly says. "We all need to feel responsible." She believes that all schools need to educate students about the climate crisis, and that politicians need to pay attention to scientists and strikers. She has been striking outside the town hall in Zeist since 2018. "Listen, think and open your eyes and see what you have been doing to the world," she says.

Anna Turns, The Guardian, 28.06.2019

---

1 to empower [ɪmˈpaʊə] jmdn. stärken **2** city hall [ˈsɪti hɔːl] Rathaus **3** township [ˈtaʊnʃɪp] Township *(von überwiegend sozial schlecht gestellten nicht weißen Menschen bewohnte, abseits der Stadt gelegene Siedlung)* **4** pupil [ˈpjuːpl] Schüler/-in

2 Story

b) *Find the words in the text and write them under the correct pictures.*

1. _____ 2. _____ 3. _____ 4. _____ 5. _____

c) *Find the words or phrases in the text that have the same (=) or opposite (↔) meaning.*

1. promise = _____
2. poor = _____
3. mild ↔ _____
4. to check = _____

d) *Take notes to complete the grid.*

who	information about project(s)	reason why they got involved
Dylan		
Yola		
Lilly		

e) *What do the three teenagers have in common?*

1. ☐ They use social media to share their projects.
2. ☐ They want the people in power to take action.
3. ☐ They found ways in their everyday lives to make a difference for the environment.
4. ☐ They work together with their local communities.

WRITING f) *Choose **one** task. Write about 120 words in your exercise book.*

1. Write a comment on why the Zulu word "ubuntu" might inspire people to become involved. Use examples to illustrate what "I am because you are" means.
2. Choose one of the young activists from the article and write an interview with him / her.

Revision B

LANGUAGE

1 Fire in a clothing factory → SB 71; G9–12

Choose a **present** or **past participle**, **gerund** or **infinitive** to complete the eyewitness report.

Not much of the building behind me is left. It was a clothing factory. I was here yesterday _____ (see) it _____ (burn) down. At first there was just smoke, but I heard somebody _____ (call) the emergency services. For several minutes I watched people _____ (carry) clothes from the building. Then the fire suddenly got worse, and I heard a small explosion _____ (break) some windows. _____ (feel) the heat of the fire on my skin, I was glad when the firefighters finally arrived. _____ (fight) their way through the flames, they managed _____ (rescue) several people _____ (trap) inside. The workers in this factory were lucky _____ (get out) alive, but many others weren't. _____ (hear) of similar disasters many times, why haven't we reacted yet? It's obvious that _____ (ignore) how our clothes are produced means _____ (contribute) to bad working conditions. That's reason enough for me to start _____ (think) about where I buy my clothes today.

LANGUAGE

2 What did he say? → SB 72; G13–15

You read parts of a blog by young environmental activist Jacob. Your friend Ira from Greenwich, who you often chat with, asks you about it. In your exercise book, write down your chat with Ira and tell her what you learned. Use suitable introductory verbs.

1. Ira — What did Jacob say what needs to be done?   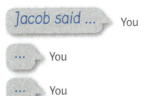 Jacob said ... You

2. Ira — Did he mention young people or what his goal is?   ... You

3. Ira — What does he plan to do next?   ... You

Jacob's environmental blog

1. "I want the politicians to take action right away. Our planet is in a crisis and we all must act in order to survive."

2. "What else can young people do to raise awareness for this problem? I hope for a world that we can still live in in a hundred years."

3. "As scientists and activists have been ignored by politicians, I am planning to strike next week."

Revision B

READING

3 SDGs: Saving the world together → SB 75; S4–5

Read the text about the UN's Sustainable Development Goals (SDGs).

In 2016 the United Nations agreed on setting new goals to make the world a better place. Covering different areas of life such as education, food, health, sustainable cities or clean energy, the altogether 17 goals were named "Sustainable Development Goals" (SDGs). The UN plans to reach them by 2030.

The SDGs have become popular, and many people – young and old – are voluntarily contributing to reaching the goals, which also symbolise how individuals can influence the world. Their activism has brought about a multitude of projects in many UN countries.

One of these people is Herman van Veen. The Dutchman works as a musician, clown, actor and storyteller, inspiring his audience with humorous lyrics. Having been speaking out for the rights of children since 1963, he believes the world could be more peaceful if the rights of children were respected. Four of the 17 SDGs focus on the rights of children to a better life: no poverty, good health and well-being, quality education, reduced inequalities. While children make up about 20 % of the world's population, a billion of them have an uncertain future. Van Veen makes people in economics, power and control responsible for not prioritising children's rights.

While children's rights play a big role in the SDGs, projects concerning the economy are also represented. The challenge here is to make our economy as eco-friendly as possible. To set an example, French diver and film producer Jérôme Delafosse and ex-marine Victorien Erussard built a large catamaran that runs on renewable power only. They and their crew sailed 9,000 km from Europe to the Caribbean to show how efficient wind and solar energy are. Sailing for 60 days, they produced their own drinking water and stopped in only two harbours to buy food.

Clearly, we as the world population are facing a huge task right now, but with the help of many activists, the SDGs may be achievable.

a) *Are these statements true, false or not in the text? Tick ✔ the correct answer.*

	true	false	not in the text
1. The UN wants to reach the SDGs within 14 years.	☐	☐	☐
2. There are lots of SDG projects in countries outside of the UN.	☐	☐	☐
3. Van Veen believes that economic aspects should not be part of the UN's SDGs.	☐	☐	☐
4. Some SDGs such as no poverty and quality education focus on children's rights.	☐	☐	☐

b) *Complete the sentences with words or phrases from the text.*

1. Delafosse and Erussard's catamaran uses _____ to cross the oceans.

2. The trip from Europe to the Caribbean took _____ and covered a distance of _____ .

3. The crew didn't have to buy _____ because they produced it themselves.

4. _____ help to improve the world and to reach _____ by 2030.

Revision B

LANGUAGE

4 Find the mistakes: The true story of palm oil → SB 75; G9, G12

Read the review on a book about how palm oil production hurts orang-utans. Decide if the underlined words or phrases are correct or not. Correct the mistakes.

This book (1) <u>described</u> how orang-utans, who are 'critically endangered', (2) <u>have to leaving</u> their habitat[1] (3) <u>because to</u> palm oil production. ('Critically endangered' (4) <u>refers for</u> (5) <u>any animal</u> which faces an (6) <u>extrem high</u> possibility of (7) <u>become</u> extinct in the wilderness.) The book also explains that (8) <u>many palm oil</u> (9) <u>is used to making</u> 'biofuel[2]', which (10) <u>are used to</u> transport, heating and many other purposes. (11) <u>According to</u> the author, (12) <u>recently</u> biofuel programmes, which are supposed to help the environment, are actually doing (13) <u>the most</u> harm (14) <u>then</u> good. (15) <u>Having produced</u> palm oil for biofuel means that forests, which are home to orang-utans and other endangered animals, (16) <u>are being cut down</u>. This is also bad for local people (17) <u>which had lived</u> in the forest or depend on (18) <u>them</u> for their jobs. This book, which has over 400 pages, perhaps (19) <u>cover</u> the issues in more detail than I really (20) <u>had needed</u>. However, it is a must for anybody who (21) <u>is interesting</u> in this subject.

1. _____
_____
_____
_____
_____
_____
_____
_____
_____
_____
_____
_____
_____
_____

LANGUAGE

5 Mixed bag: The 'Energy Observer' → SB 75; G9, G12

A crew member's diary tells us more about the 'Energy Observer', a large catamaran which was designed to research renewable technologies. Complete her diary entry.

I _____ on board the Energy Observer for 50 days now. Sometimes I still _____ believe I'm really here. I still remember how it all _____. A few years ago, I read about a project that _____ two French guys. They _____ (build) an emission-free ship at the time _____ should _____ the power of the ocean, wind and sun instead of _____ fuels. I, _____ a diver and scientist, _____ wanted to take part in the project and a year later I got on board! _____ I love _____ about the ship is that if it is cloudy and windless (which _____ regularly), the motor _____ hydrogen[3] for up to six days. Today we _____ diving and saw several large sharks _____ just below our ship. The underwater world _____ surprising me! I _____ wish for a more interesting job!

1 habitat ['hæbɪtæt] Lebensraum 2 biofuel ['baɪəʊfjuːəl] Biokraftstoff 3 hydrogen ['haɪdrədʒən] Wasserstoff

Text smart 2

Argumentative texts

VOCABULARY

1 Linking, structuring, commenting → SB 77

a) Put these words/phrases in the correct boxes. For each category, add at least two more words.

eventually | actually | although | second(ly) | since | frankly | unless | possibly
on top of that | therefore | otherwise | obviously | while | on the one/other hand

linking ideas	commenting/giving opinions	structuring/ordering

b) Link these sentences (or start new ones) about a nurse's job with words/phrases from a).

1. Nurses work very hard every day. They make less money than most people think.
   _____

2. Caring for others is an important task in our society. Nurses should be paid fairly.
   _____

3. A nurse's main job is to care for sick people. They assist doctors and do paperwork.
   _____

4. We need to pay nurses better. Some may leave their jobs.
   _____

WRITING

2 Writing a topic sentence → SB 77; S9

a) Look at the following topic sentences. For each pair, explain which one is better and why.

1a) In fact, a vegetarian diet is significantly better for one's health, so people would profit from becoming vegetarians.
b) Vegetarian dishes include Indian curries, salads and also a lot of tasty desserts.

2a) There are many obese children in our school, so the government should do something about it.
b) Since the number of obese children is rising in the US, parents need to know about the main reasons for this problem.

3a) Of course, some influencers are really famous, but I still think it's a stupid thing to do.
b) First, following influencers on social media can pose serious dangers for young people.

b) Read the following paragraphs. Add a suitable topic sentence for each one.

1. _____

_____

They can be taken along everywhere and fit into almost any pocket. That way mobile phones help us find our way in a city or contact someone at any time. This shows that mobile phones provide mobility and freedom to their users.

2. _____

_____

Of course, there are different ways to do so. While some may argue that exams are not a perfect system to evaluate students' abilities, they are currently the best system we have. And obviously, we need such a system.

WRITING

3 An essay on cyberbullying → SB 79; S7–9

a) Look at the outline for a **persuasive pro-pro, con-con essay** with this title: "Cyberbullying is a fact of life, and nothing can be done to stop it". Put these notes in the correct places in the grid. Then look at the tip box in d) on the following page and add your own ideas for the conclusion.

change laws to fight cyberbullying | online content difficult to control | harsher punishments for bullies | impossible to delete completely | cyberbullying is a common problem, affects esp. teenagers | people can be educated to change their behaviour | ask: can it really not be stopped?

introduction		
– cyberbullying: examples + definition –		
main part		
	pros	**cons**
argument 1		
support for argument 1 (examples, statistics etc.)	recent German study: nearly 1/3 of teens got wrong / offending content; about 40 % know sb who has experienced cyberbullying	a) force websites to block bullies and to delete offending content b)
argument 2		
support for argument 2 (examples, statistics etc.)	a) can be shared very quickly + reaches large audience b)	workshops about 'online rules': communication rules apply online too; careful with private information
conclusion		

forty-nine 49

Text smart 2

b) *Which of these introductions is better? Explain why.*

A Have you ever received offending chat messages? Has anyone ever posted embarrassing photos of you? These are acts of cyberbullying, a form of online harassment that seems impossible to stop since using social media has become an important part of everyday life. But is that really true?

B Today most people use social media and cyberbullying is a terrible problem which affects lots of people, especially teenagers like me. I hate cyberbullying because it's an awful thing which should be stopped as soon as possible.

c) *Now look at these first paragraphs. Explain which one is better and why.*

A A recent German study supports my next argument. It says that lots of German teenagers received wrong or offending content and lots of them also know someone who has experienced cyberbullying themselves. That's horrible, isn't it? I think we must do something now because it's a problem for so many people and also because online content is really difficult to control.

B Unfortunately, cyberbullying is a common problem that affects many people, especially teenagers. For example, a recent study from Germany found that nearly one third of German teenagers received wrong or offending content themselves and about 40 % know someone who has experienced cyberbullying. These numbers illustrate that cyberbullying definitely is part of many young people's lives.

d) *Finish the essay. Write the paragraph for pro-argument 2, the paragraphs for the con-arguments, and the conclusion in your exercise book (about 250 words).*

Tip

The conclusion restates the main question or sums up your opinion. You may also give an outlook on possible solutions / consequences or encourage readers to reach their own conclusion. **Do not introduce new arguments.**

e) *Exchange texts with a partner. Peer-edit each other's work with the help of this checklist.*

CHECKLIST

1. **Structure**
   - Is each argument and supporting information (examples etc.) in one paragraph?
   - Do the paragraphs start with a suitable topic sentence?
   - Are paragraphs and sentences logically linked?
2. **Style**
   - no short forms
   - neutral style (no exaggerations, no personal comments)
   - no unnecessary repetition

Tip

Don't forget to give **constructive feedback**:
- Start with what you liked about your partner's essay.
- Always try to give tips how mistakes or problematic parts can be improved.

Across cultures 3

VOCABULARY

1 Make your voice heard! → SB 80

a) *How can people make their voices heard? Make a mind map.*

- _____
- *signing a* _____
- _____
- _____
- *joining a* _____
- _____
- _____
- *writing a* _____

You can make your voice heard by ...

b) *Compare your ideas with those of your partner. For each of your ideas in a) think of a situation in which this is an effective way to make your voice heard.*

VOCABULARY

2 Make a difference! → SB 81; S1, S14

a) *Complete the dialogue about political activism with the correct forms of these verbs.*

| believe | change | decide | depend | do one's bit | draw |
| feel | get involved | make (3x) | mean | stand up | understand |

Guy: Do you really think that being a political activist actually _____ a difference?

Annabel: Of course, I do, but that's not the main reason I _____ to _____ in protests and student politics.

Guy: No? So what was the reason?

Annabel: In my opinion, if you _____ strongly about something, you should _____ for your beliefs. You have to at least *try* to _____ the world a better place.

Guy: So you're just _____ a statement about what you _____ in?

Annabel: No, that's not what I _____. I think I _____ to try to make life a little better for me, you and everyone else. Maybe it'll help, maybe it won't. But at least I'll have tried.

Guy: Do you think protest stunts are the best way to _____ people's attention to problems?

Annabel: It _____. It's not enough just to say there's a problem. You need to help people to _____ the issues. Then they're more likely to _____ their behaviour.

b) *Research a protest stunt online. In a small group, give a two-minute presentation. Then discuss if you think it was a good way to make one's voice heard.*

3 Check-in

Unit 3 The good life?

VOCABULARY

1 A good life to me is ... → SB 82

a) *Everybody defines a good life differently. Match these words with their opposites.*

adventurous   challenging   relaxed   spiritual   simple   spontaneous

1. planned ↔ _____
2. materialistic ↔ _____
3. boring ↔ _____
4. busy ↔ _____
5. easy ↔ _____
6. glamorous ↔ _____

b) *In your exercise book, use words from a) to write in about 120 words what a good life means to you.*

SPEAKING

2 Life's good when ... → SB 82; S13

Choose 1–2 of the quotes and discuss them with a partner. What do the quotes mean? Do you agree or disagree with them?

1. Build your own dreams, or someone else will hire[1] you to build theirs.
   Farrah Gray, businessman

2. He who does not get fun and enjoyment out of every day, needs to reorganize his life. George Adams, jazz musician

3. The good life is built with good relationships.
   Robert J. Waldinger, psychiatrist[2]

4. Rules should always be bent[3], if not broken. It's the only way to have any fun.
   Alyson Noël, writer

VOCABULARY

3 My dream job → SB 83

Complete Arianna's social media comment about her dream job.

Arianna   19:30

For me, the most important thing is being interested in the professional _____ that I'll work in. It must be f_____, m_____ work with which I can make a _____. _____ is important too, of course. Nobody wants to do the same thing every day. Also, I don't want to look at a computer screen all day. I'd like to be _____ in dealing with people _____ to face. That's why I think a job in _____ and social _____ might be the right one for me. I'd love to be a doctor one day.

1 to hire sb [ˈhaɪə] jdn. einstellen 2 psychiatrist [saɪˈkaɪətrɪst] Psychiater/-in 3 *to bend [bend] beugen *(Regeln, Gesetze)*

MEDIATION

4 A job for a day → SB 85; S15

An der Schule deiner Freundin Alina aus den USA gab es eine Jobmesse. Sie war überrascht, dass die meisten ihrer Mitschüler/-innen nur mit Unternehmen gesprochen haben, die "typische" Jungen- bzw. Mädchenberufe angeboten haben. Alina würde gerne wissen, ob es in Deutschland ähnliche Veranstaltungen gibt. Nutze die folgenden Informationen und einen der persönlichen Erfahrungsberichte, um ihr eine E-Mail (ca. 150 Wörter) über den Girls'/Boys' Day zu schreiben. Erkläre ihr, was am Girls'/Boys' Day gemacht wird, was die Ziele sind und was schon erreicht wurde.

Tschüss, Klischees

Für Mädchen und Jungen war es ein spannender Einblick in für sie bislang ungewohnte Berufe, für die Unternehmen und Institutionen eine sehr gute Möglichkeit, praxisnah den Nachwuchs zu fördern: Der Girls' Day und Boys' Day versammelte wieder für einen Tag Zehntausende Jugendliche, Unternehmen und Institutionen unter dem Motto „Tschüss, Klischees!". Denn es gibt sie noch immer: Berufe mit geringem Frauen- oder Männeranteil. Einen Impuls gegen den Einfluss von Geschlechterstereotypen auf die Berufs- und Studienwahl setzten in diesem Jahr wieder mehr als 130.000 Schülerinnen und Schüler aus ganz Deutschland.

Am Girls' Day können Schülerinnen Einblick in Berufsfelder erhalten, die Mädchen im Prozess der Berufsorientierung nur selten in Betracht ziehen. In erster Linie bieten technische Unternehmen und Abteilungen, sowie Hochschulen, Forschungszentren und ähnliche Einrichtungen am Girls' Day Veranstaltungen für Mädchen an. Anhand von praktischen Beispielen erleben die Teilnehmerinnen in Laboren, Büros und Werkstätten, wie interessant und spannend diese Arbeit sein kann.

Am Boys' Day können Jungen Berufe kennenlernen, in denen bislang nur wenige Männer arbeiten. Das sind vor allem Berufe aus dem sozialen, erzieherischen und pflegerischen Bereich. Außerdem können sie an Angeboten zur Lebensplanung, zu Männlichkeitsbildern und zu Sozialkompetenzen teilnehmen.

Sowohl der Girls' Day als auch der Boys' Day richten sich an Schülerinnen und Schüler ab Klasse 5. "Unsere Erhebung belegt: Der Girls' Day und Boys' Day wirken. Die Aktionstage erweitern das Berufs- und Studienwahlspektrum der Mädchen und Jungen und unterstützen sie bei der Berufs- und Studienorientierung. Auch die teilnehmenden Unternehmen und Institutionen haben einen großen Nutzen. Für sie funktionieren die Aktionstage als Instrumente der Öffentlichkeitsarbeit und Nachwuchsgewinnung", so Romy Stühmeier, Leiterin der Bundeskoordinierungsstelle Boys' Day – Jungen-Zukunftstag.

Girls' Day – Lilly:
Ich bin ein Computer-Nerd und habe mich deshalb total gefreut an der Universität Augsburg an dem Programm Informatik B teilzunehmen. Für mich ist der Girls' Day eine großartige Gelegenheit, meinen Interessen nachgehen zu können und neue Gebiete zu erkunden. Durch den Girls' Day weiß ich jetzt, dass mein Traum, mal mit Computern zu arbeiten, genauso cool ist, wie ich mir das vorgestellt habe. Das Problem dabei ist, dass ich lieber heute als morgen damit anfangen würde, aber ich muss noch ein paar Jahre warten. Aber jetzt weiß ich auch, wofür mein Abi gut sein wird! Ich habe jetzt jede Menge Motivation!

Boys' Day – Jeshrun:
In der 1b erwartete mich (Zitat Frau Kirchhoff) „die verrückteste Klasse der Welt". Als die Kinder mich sahen, sprangen sie auf mich, stellten mir Fragen, zerrten an meiner Kleidung, doch mit gemeinsamen Kräften konnten Frau Kirchhoff und ich sie bändigen. Der Unterricht verlief weniger turbulent: Die Schüler wiederholten das Alphabet, lernten dazu die Anwendung des Buchstaben B, übten das Lesen in der Fibel. Ich zolle jedem der Grundschullehrer Respekt, denn ein solcher Job ist von Konzentration, Übersicht und Geduld geprägt, und diese jeden Tag zu jeder Stunde an den Tag zu bringen, ist eine bemerkenswerte Leistung.

Girls' Day- und Boys' Day-Webseite, 2019

3 Station 1

WRITING

5 Are you mad? → SB 86; S7, S16

Write a description of this cartoon and explain its message (about 170 words). Use your exercise book.

Useful phrases

risk of being unsuccessful | become famous | earn/lose money | hard work | chaotic life | positive/negative experience | do what you are passionate about

"You want to join a rock band? Are you mad?"

"You want to join a start-up? Are you mad?"

MEDIATION

6 Looking at adverts for work experience[1] → SB 86; S15

Am schwarzen Brett deiner Schule hängt ein Aushang mit Praktikumsstellen. Der/die britische Gastschüler/-in, der/die für ein halbes Jahr bei dir wohnt, versteht noch nicht so gut Deutsch, möchte sich aber in den Ferien auf eine der Stellen bewerben. Hilf ihm/ihr, die Anzeigen zu verstehen. Verteilt die Rollen und macht euch Notizen. Spielt dann die Szene und wechselt die Rollen ab.

Role card A (britische/-r Austauschschüler/-in)
Du ...
- fragst nach dem Inhalt der Anzeigen
- stellst Nachfragen zu den Dingen, die dir wichtig sind (z. B. Bezahlung, selbstständiges Arbeiten)
- entscheidest dich nach Abwägung deiner Interessen und Fähigkeiten für eine der Stellen und fragst nach der Meinung deines Partners/ deiner Partnerin

Role card B (deutsche/-r Schüler/-in)
Du ...
- stellst deinem/deiner Partner/-in kurz die Praktika und deren Aufgabenbereiche vor
- beantwortest Nachfragen
- gibst einen begründeten Ratschlag, ob die Stelle zu ihm / ihr passen würde

Großes Herz für Vierbeiner?

Wir suchen: Schüler/-innen für ein Nachmittagspraktikum (Mo–Do, 15–18 Uhr) in unserer Kleintierklinik

Wir bieten: Modern ausgestattete Klinik, offenes Praxisteam, intensive Einarbeitung

Voraussetzungen: Gesundheitliche Eignung (keine Tierhaarallergie), gute Noten in Biologie, Einfühlungsvermögen, Zuverlässigkeit

Bei deinem Praktikum unterstützt du das Team vor allem bei der Organisation der Praxisabläufe. Du vereinbarst Termine mit den Kunden/Kundinnen und empfängst sie und die tierischen Patienten. Zudem bereitest du die Untersuchungsräume vor und fütterst die Tiere auf der Krankenstation. Nach der Einarbeitung führst du diese Routinetätigkeiten selbstständig aus. Bitte bedenke bei deiner Bewerbung, dass wir eine Tierklinik und kein Streichelzoo sind!

Praktikumszeitraum: mind. 3 Wochen
Vergütung: 13€ / Stunde

Praktikum KFZ-Mechatroniker/-in

Du interessierst dich für Kraftfahrzeuge und hast ein gutes technisches Verständnis? Dann ist ein Praktikum bei uns in der Werkstatt genau das Richtige für dich. Du bist nicht richtig, wenn du zwei linke Hände hast und lieber am Schreibtisch sitzen möchtest. Bei uns kann es auch mal schmutzig werden, dafür sind Spaß und Teamwork garantiert.

Inhalte deines Praktikums:
- Prüfung, Diagnose und Instandsetzung von Übungsmotoren
- Unterstützung des Teams bei Carchecks (z. B. Bremsen prüfen, Ölwechsel)
- Recherchieren von Informationen zur Durchführung von Reparaturen

Schicke uns deine Bewerbungsunterlagen zu und werde für zwei Wochen Teil des Teams. Als Praktikumsgehalt bieten wir dir den gesetzlichen Mindestlohn. Deine Arbeitszeiten sind Di–Sa von 7:30–15 Uhr.

---

[1] work experience (BE) [ˈwɜːkˌɪkˌspɪəriəns] Schülerpraktikum

Station 1

VOCABULARY 7 Curriculum Vitae → SB 86

○ Complete Jason's CV for a job as a management assistant at a leisure centre with these words and phrases.

chance   communication (2x)   contact   customers
decision   education   experience   interests
organisational skills   passionate   position   present
references   reliability   request   responsibility

Tip

When writing a CV, choose a font (e.g. Arial, Helvetica), font size (12 point) and line spacing that makes it easy to read. Don't mix them up because it can look messy. You can still use underline, CAPITALS, **boldface** or *italics* for words and phrases. Leave a line of space between each paragraph. Try to fit your CV onto one page.

JASON STEPHENS

_____ DETAILS

phone: 01173 990621
e-mail: [mail address]
address: 104 Walton Park Road, Bristol, BS9 8QJ

PERSONAL PROFILE

I am _____ about sports. Not only do I love playing on a team, but I also love working in a team. I am looking for a _____ which will give me the _____ to use my _____ skills and to work with sports in some way. I have _____ in sports management from helping to run my college football team. I took _____ for arranging matches against other colleges, which required _____ and _____.

_____ are available on _____.

SKILLS

- _____
- Organisation
- _____ making
- Basic graphic design

_____

- Sports (football, running)
- Cooking
- Camping

WORK EXPERIENCE

- 2019– _____ : sales assistant, Pound Paradise, Bristol
- Assisted with the running of the shop
- Advised _____

_____

- 2017–2020: Grange Rise Sixth Form College, Bristol
  A levels in Sport and Physical Education (B) & Leisure Studies (B)
- 2012–2017: Chatterton Comprehensive School, Bristol
- 2006–2012: Castle Hill Primary School, Bristol

3 Station 1

LANGUAGE

8 Application rules → SB 87

Complete this text about the application process at a summer camp with these **linking adverbs / adverbs of comment**. There's one extra word.

`additionally` `furthermore` `however (2x)` `in fact` `luckily` `nevertheless` `therefore` `unfortunately`

> Working as an assistant camp counsellor with Sunny Valley Summer Camps shouldn't be 'just a summer job'. _____, we offer workshops for people who are interested in becoming camp counsellors. _____, there is not just one start date – you can join our programme at any time. Most of our first-time assistant camp counsellors have only recently left school. _____, we also welcome applications from older candidates. We no longer accept job applications by mail. _____, applying online is simple and easy to do. Please note that we cannot accept attachments larger than 5 MB. _____, very few CVs are larger than that, but do check before you send. _____, check the content of your CV before you send it. You will not be able to resend it. _____, we also cannot reply to any individual requests. _____, you may find any extra information you are looking for on the FAQs page.

WRITING

9 An application letter → SB 87; S6–8

Rewrite Jason's application letter for management assistant in a formal style.
If possible, write it on a computer.

(Write the address and contact details as on the CV in Exercise 7)
(Write today's date.)

Andrea Hawkins
Bristol Leisure and Sports Services Ltd.
14–18 Aylesbury Road
Bristol
BS3 9GN

Job in your leisure centre

Hi Andrea,

I'm writing about a summer job I saw on jobs4U.uk. I want to help your leisure centre's management to organise sports activities and deal with customers.

I'm 19, and I've just left sixth form. At the moment, I'm still working in a shop, but that's about to finish. With a bit of luck, I'll get a job which goes a lot better with who I am as a person, and which I'll also be able to continue part-time once I've started my course in sports management at the local uni.

I've got a couple of A levels – one in Leisure Studies & one in Sport and Physical Education (I got B for both of them). Also, I learned a bit about management when I was helping to run the college football team in sixth form.

Thanks a lot for checking out my application. I can come for an interview any Monday or Tuesday – they're my days off. I'm really looking forward to getting your reply!

Best wishes,
Jason :-)

(Don't miss the CV in the attachment!)

Station 1 3

LISTENING **10** **An interview for an interview** → SB 88; S12

A7 🔊 a) *Listen to the first part of a phone call between Ella Lewis and Rima Hassan of Action Summer UK. Tick ✔ the things Rima is asking about.*

1. ☐ Ella's education and qualifications
2. ☐ Her work experience
3. ☐ Her hobbies
4. ☐ How Ella describes herself on her CV
5. ☐ When she is available for work
6. ☐ Why she wants to be a summer camp counsellor

b) *Listen to the first part again and answer the questions. Take notes.*

1. What is Ella's current job and what skill does it especially require? _____
   _____

2. What does Ella tell Rima about the last event she organised? _____
   _____
   _____

3. When does Rima especially need people to work for Action Summer UK? _____
   _____

A8 🔊 c) *Listen to the second part of the phone call. Take notes about the interview.*

When: _____

Where: _____

What to bring: _____

SPEAKING **11** **A phone call** → SB 88; S13

Do a role play: Andrea Hawkins (partner A) is calling Jason Stephens (partner B) to invite him for an interview as management assistant.

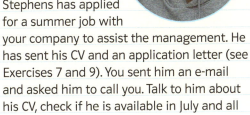

Partner A:

You are Andrea Hawkins of Bristol Leisure and Sports Services Ltd. Jason Stephens has applied for a summer job with your company to assist the management. He has sent his CV and an application letter (see Exercises 7 and 9). You sent him an e-mail and asked him to call you. Talk to him about his CV, check if he is available in July and all of August. Invite him for an interview.

Partner B:

You are Jason Stephens and you have applied for a summer job at Bristol Leisure and Sports Services Ltd. In her e-mail, Andrea Hawkins asked you to call her. When you speak to her, be prepared to talk about your CV (see Exercises 7 and 9) and to explain when you are available (on holiday in the first week of July, but available for the rest of the summer).

3 Station 2

LISTENING

12 The internship¹ → SB 91; S6–8, S12

A 9–10

a) *It's Maya's first day at her internship at a local newspaper. Listen to the conversation between her and Chad, who is showing her around. Tick ✔ the topics they're talking about.*

1. ☐ Maya's experience
2. ☐ a meeting with the boss
3. ☐ working hours
4. ☐ privacy rules
5. ☐ breaks
6. ☐ what to do when sick
7. ☐ mobile phone policy
8. ☐ smoking
9. ☐ vacation

b) *Listen to part 1 and complete the text.*

Both Maya and Chad were _____ at their high school. At the Portland Times, Maya will help the team _____ and _____ articles, but she will also get to know other jobs, for example in _____ or _____, to get a good overview. But, just like Chad, Maya will mainly work for the _____.

c) *Complete Maya's notes.*

Intranet (like a _____ for the newspaper)
- useful information, e.g. _____ and _____
- _____ for new employees
- _____ every day

Start of working day
- usually around ____:____ / ____:____
- start _____ and _____,
 then _____ the time I've arrived
 in the _____ recording system

d) *Listen to part 2 and underline the correct answers. More than one answer may be correct.*

1. Coffee breaks are good to — check social media. | move a bit. | get to know people.
2. Most employees take a lunch break for — no longer than 20 minutes. | 30 minutes. | a minimum of 40 minutes.
3. For lunch Maya can — bring food from home. | go to the newspaper's cafeteria. | get something from a restaurant nearby.

e) *Answer these questions. Take notes.*

1. What should Maya do when she is sick? _____
2. What should she do at the end of the day? _____
3. Who should she ask when she has any questions? _____

WRITING

f) *Think about an internship you would like to do and write a diary entry (about 100 words) about how your first day was.*

¹ internship [ˈɪntɜːnʃɪp] Praktikum

Station 2 3

LANGUAGE **13** It's my duty to speak out → SB 92; G17

○ a) *Look at this defining and non-defining relative clause.*
○ *Explain the difference in meaning.*
○
1. Emma Watson's brother who also had a small role in the *Harry Potter* movies appeared in a big fashion campaign with her.
2. Emma Watson's brother, who also had a small role in the *Harry Potter* movies, appeared in a big fashion campaign with her.

b) *Read this text about Emma Watson and have a closer look at the relative clauses in the text.*

1. Use different colours to mark the defining and the non-defining relative clauses.
2. Add commas where necessary.
3. Put brackets around the relative pronouns which can be left out to make a contact clause.

The British actress and activist Emma Watson who was born in Paris in 1990 became world famous for her role as Hermione Granger in the *Harry Potter* movies. Now, Watson whose
5   dream it was to become an actress from an early age on is one of the highest-paid actresses in the world. Being famous gives her a platform which other people don't have and so she feels it's her duty to speak
10   out about social and environmental issues like women's rights and sustainable fashion. In 2014 she became a UN Women Goodwill Ambassador[1] which earned her a place on the *Time* magazine's list of the 100 most
15   influential[2] people in 2015. She also helped launching[3] the *HeForShe* campaign which is a UN programme to include men in the conversation about gender equality. But her work doesn't stop there. Emma Watson also
20   started a feminist book club which has over 400,000 followers on social media and she even helped launch an advice hotline for women who experienced sexual harassment at work. In one of her more recent acting roles, she plays Meg March in the movie *Little Women* which is 25
based on a novel. The plot is set in New England during the 1860s and the story follows the four March sisters who are struggling to find their way between society's expectations and their personal desires. The character which Watson 30
plays chooses to be a wife and mother. This is a decision that may not seem very feminist to some people. For Watson, however, Meg's decision shows that there's more than one way to be a feminist which is an idea a lot of 35
people still don't understand completely. Another project that she was recently involved in was the Fashion Footprint Calculator. The calculator is an online tool which shows the impact that a person's fashion choices have on the climate. 40

c) *Reread the text and complete the information about Emma Watson's career.*

Emma Watson's career is anything but ordinary. Not only did she know that she wants to become

an actress from _____, but she even became one of the world's

_____ actresses. However, Watson isn't just an actress. She also is

an _____ speaking mainly about _____ rights and sustainable

_____. Some of her most recent projects were an _____ in

the _____ *Little Women* and an online tool which calculates the environmental

_____ of a person's _____ choices.

1 ambassador [amˈbæsədə] Botschafter/-in ○ 2 influential [ˌɪnfluˈenʃl] einflussreich ○ 3 to launch [lɔːnʃ] starten

Station 2

LANGUAGE **14** **Work experience** → SB 92; G17

○ Read some advice from an employer to young people who want to join the company for work experience.
○ In your exercise book, rewrite the advice with the information in the yellow boxes.
○ Use **relative clauses** and remember to add commas for the **non-defining relative clauses**.

| we are offering to you | you are applying for | you can post or fill in online | you have been given |

| will last up to 15 minutes | will ask you some pre-interview questions | you will hopefully understand |

| will be in London, Birmingham or Glasgow | will result in the application not being considered |

Applying for work experience with JMBC

When you apply for work experience with our company, first of all make sure the position **(1)** matches your experience and qualifications. Then check that the application form **(2)** has been fully and correctly completed. Some people forget to provide essential information **(3)**. Before we offer you a face-to-face interview, you will be called by the manager of our work experience programme **(4)**. During this call **(5)** you will be asked about your present situation and your hopes for the future. If you are then offered a face-to-face interview **(6)** we will pay your travel expenses[1]. The reimbursement[2] of your costs can take 10–12 days **(7)**. If your application is successful, you will be informed of the general type of work experience **(8)**. If you accept, you will not be informed of the exact role **(9)** until you arrive on the first morning.

SPEAKING **15** **The value of education** → SB 92; S17

a) *Choose one of the diagrams and describe it to your partner. Talk about the connection between the two diagrams.*

b) *Discuss possible reasons for the differences in earnings. Do you think these differences are justified?*

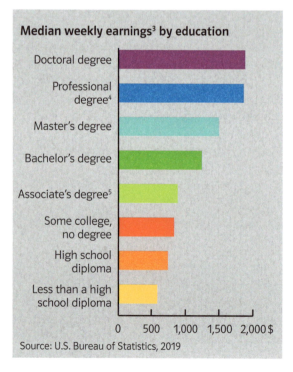

Median weekly earnings[3] by education
Source: U.S. Bureau of Statistics, 2019

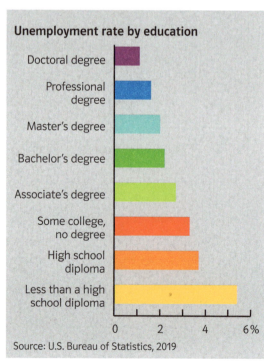

Unemployment rate by education
Source: U.S. Bureau of Statistics, 2019

c) *Do these statistics influence your plans for after school?*

1 expenses [ɪkˈspensɪz] Kosten ○ **2** reimbursement [ˌriːɪmˈbɜːsmənt] Erstattung ○ **3** earnings [ˈɜːnɪŋz] Einkommen ○ **4** professional degree [prəˈfeʃnl dɪˈɡriː] Doktor *(praktische Studienausrichtung)* ○ **5** associate's degree [əˈsəʊʃiəts dɪˈɡriː] spezialisierende Zusatzqualifikation nach der Highschool

Station 2 / 3

LANGUAGE 16 First day on the job → SB 93; G18, G20

a) *Calvin posted this story about his first day at a new job in an online forum. Rewrite the phrases in **bold** to add emphasis.*

> I was 15 minutes late on my first day in my first job. **(1) I've never been so embarrassed. (2) I'd no sooner arrived than I was apologising for something.** I told a woman who seemed to manage things there a long boring (and not actually true) story about how I missed the bus to work. **(3) I only realised she was not the boss when she suddenly looked at me in surprise. (4) That moment my face turned completely red.**
>
> "What?" she said, "Sorry, I wasn't listening. I was thinking about lizards. Amazing animals. Anyway, hi, my name's Lulu. I keep the computers going."
>
> **(5) I had hardly finished apologising again when my new boss walked through the door. (6) She was not only arriving nearly half an hour late, but she was carrying a skateboard.** I couldn't believe it. **(7) My boss was late, not me.**
>
> "9:25," she said, looking at her watch, "Better than usual. But there are more important things in life than worrying about the minute hand[1] on a clock, that's what I always say." **(8) My expectations have rarely changed so quickly.** I suddenly knew that this was going to be rather an unusual place to work.

1. Never have I _____

_____

_____

_____

_____

_____

_____

_____

b) *To practise how rewriting changes the emphasis, read the rewritten sentences to a partner. Take turns.*

LANGUAGE 17 Safety rules → SB 93; G19

a) *In your exercise book, rewrite this introduction to a safety announcement. Add **do / does / did** for emphasis in each of the seven places possible. Change the form of words in the text where necessary.*

> I understand that you're very excited and want to start your first day of work experience, but before you begin, I need to explain the safety rules of this office. Every one of you really needs to remember that this is a place of work, not a school. You don't need to worry about safety every minute of every day, but you need to be sensible. Everybody here has to take responsibility for their own safety, and for the safety of others. We had some problems with the last work experience group who were here, so we ask you to listen *very* carefully to this announcement.

A11 b) *Listen to the announcement to check your rewritten introduction. Then read it out loud with the emphasis on the correct words.*

[1] hand [hænd] Zeiger

3 Station 2

LANGUAGE

18 Find the mistakes: Solutions for everyday problems → SB 93; G18

Read the article about Mihir Garimella, a young inventor from Pittsburgh, Pennsylvania.
Decide if the underlined words / phrases are correct or not. Correct the mistakes.

Mihir Garimella (1) is developing technological solutions for everyday problems since he (2) has been about 10. Mihir's big breakthrough came when he (3) became interested in fruit flies[1]. (4) Forgotten some bananas in the kitchen when they (5) left for vacation, the family found their house full of flies when they (6) returned four weeks later. (7) Mihir had no sooner tried to hit the flies (and failed) than he became curious and began (9) researching the flies. In the end, he used his results (10) to build a drone modelled on the insects. Mihir's drone is designed to help in search and rescue missions, (11) for exemple after earthquakes[2] or during fires. (12) Sure, Mihir's curiosity and creativity will lead him to build (13) much other great and useful inventions.

1. _____
   _____
   _____
   _____
   _____
   _____
   _____
   _____

LANGUAGE

19 Mixed bag: A summer job for the future? → SB 93; G18, G20

Put in the missing words and phrases to complete the text about how Sierra's summer job turned into a career.

My career as an IT expert _____ at our local electronics store _____ I was 16. _____ a summer job _____ year was high on my list of priorities. _____ out more _____ 20 applications, I got called in for exactly one interview and _____ a job _____ a cashier[3]. "The job can be boring", the manager warned me, "Your only task is _____ behind the checkout." No sooner _____ I _____ to work at the checkout than I started _____ (comment) on each customer's purchase and _____ suggestions. After _____ me for a while, the manager announced, "_____ you are really good at is customer service. From now on, you're a salesperson!" Working in sales, I _____ to talk to the customers and _____ individual solutions for their problems. Now, almost fifteen years _____, I _____ at a small IT company, where I basically still do the same thing: understanding _____ our customers are looking for and finding answers for their problems. But if it _____ for my summer job that year, I _____ as good at explaining difficult concepts to our customers as I am today.

1 fruit fly [fruːt flaɪ] Fruchtfliege ○ **2** earthquake [ˈɜːkweɪk] Erdbeben ○ **3** cashier [kæʃˈɪə] Kassierer/-in

Skills 3

SKILLS 20 **Conduct interviews with applicants and panels** → SB 94; S8, S12

A 12 🔊 a) *Listen to Josh's job interview and complete the text.*

Josh is being interviewed for the position as a _____ and _____ at a summer camp. Josh applied for the job because it _____ and the payment is good. When asked for his strengths, Josh says that he is a good _____. However, his weakness is that he can be a bit _____ sometimes.

b) *Listen again and name the six things that Josh does wrong.*

_____
_____
_____
_____

c) *Replace the phrases that Josh said in the interview with more formal ones.*

1. Is that correct? – **Yeah, that's right.**

   _____

2. How would you describe your strengths? – **Er, I don't know.**

   _____

3. … find out who wants to go skateboarding. **That kind of thing.**

   _____

4. We'll let you know of our decision by e-mail. – **OK, cool.**

   _____

SKILLS 21 **Typical interview questions** → SB 94

a) *Match the four job interview questions with these beginnings of answers.*

1. What made you decide to apply?
2. What would you bring to the job?
3. How would you describe your strengths?
4. What's your biggest weakness?

a) I have a lot of experience with / in …
b) I can sometimes be a little too …
c) My main talent is …
d) I have always wanted to work in / for …
e) I would be a reliable hard-working member of the team, and I would always …
f) I'm not always as … as I'd like to be.
g) I'm known for being a good …
h) When I saw your advertisement, I immediately thought …

b) *In your exercise book, complete each sentence with your ideas.*

3 Story

VOCABULARY 22 Tips from a career coach → SB 100

○ *A career coach posted these interview tips on her website. Use the correct form of these words to complete the tips. There are two extra words.*

to assign	firm	gentle	gestures
to hesitate	ordinary	to permit	puzzled
shift	satisfied	unpredictable

Interviews aren't _____ situations, so make sure you're prepared. Start out with a polite

greeting and speak in a _____ voice. Voice as well as _____ are very important.

Also, some interviewers like to ask _____ questions just to see how candidates react.

If time _____, don't _____ to ask some questions too, e.g. about the tasks

you _____. In any case the worst thing to do is to have a _____

expression on your face and to _____ around in your seat.

READING 23 A natural talent → SB 101; S2, S4–5, S10–11

○ **a)** *Read the text about an unusual job interview and do the exercises on the following page.*

David got off the bus outside the hospital. He was cross with himself because he was feeling so nervous. Why be nervous? It was just an ordinary interview with some ordinary people
5 for an ordinary job. A very ordinary job. Perhaps it was because he knew he had to lie that he was nervous.

"Why do you want to work in hospital administration?" he imagined the interviewer
10 saying.

"I think it would match my skills and interests very well," he imagined himself lying. The true answer was "I have absolutely zero interest in hospital administration, but I need a
15 job and I need it now."

David walked into the big, gloomy Victorian building. One of dozens of signs pointed to 'Human Resources Department.' He walked along a long dark corridor which smelled of
20 disinfectant. It wasn't that he had a problem with hospitals, but *administration*? Drama and music had always been his favourite subjects at school. He had always imagined that one day he would …

25 "Can I help you?" said a voice. David had arrived at the Human Resources Department.

"I've come for an interview," he said to the woman behind the desk. "David Turner. Ten thirty."

30 "Interview Room 2. Wait till you're called."

Outside Interview Room 1, there were two young women and a young man of a similar age to David, sitting on plastic chairs and looking uncomfortable. Outside Interview Room 2 there was nobody. No sooner had he sat down than 35 the door opened. A youngish woman's face appeared and smiled at him.

"Ah, somebody's here at last," she said. "Wonderful. Please do come in."

David stood up and walked into the room. 40 As well as the woman who had opened the door, there was an older woman and a middle-aged man. They were sitting behind a large desk with a computer in the middle of it. The younger woman walked to an empty chair behind the 45 desk and sat down with them.

"So you're the 10:30," said the older woman. She looked at the computer screen and moved the mouse. "Hmm. I can't find a 10:30. We've been having lots of problems with the computer 50 system. What's your name?"

"David Turner."

The woman put the name into the computer. "And your address and phone number?" David supplied them. 55

"OK, well now we've got that problem solved, we can start," said the woman. "Do you want to go first, Tony?" she asked the man.

"OK, Geraldine," said Tony. "I'll start." He turned to speak to David. "Do you know a lot of 60 jokes?"

David's feelings of nervousness turned to total confusion. *"What!?"* he wanted to say.

"Um … excuse me?" he said.

"Do you know a lot of jokes?" asked the man 65 seriously.

64 sixty-four

It must be some kind of test, thought David. To see how he reacted to a weird question.

"Well, actually, I do," he said. "I'm a big fan of comedy. I write the best jokes I've heard in a little book, so I don't forget them. I love telling them to other people."

"Can you give me an example?" asked Tony.

"Sure," said David. "Patient: 'Doctor, Doctor! I get a terrible pain in my eye every time I drink coffee.' Doctor: 'Have you tried taking the spoon out of the cup?'"

Tony nodded with a satisfied expression on his face.

"Angela," asked Geraldine to the younger woman. "Do you have a question?"

"Do you know many magic tricks?" Angela asked David.

Another weird question? Well, OK …

"Not very many," David said. "I was very interested in learning magic tricks when I was a kid. I can still do them, but they're not great. I think people enjoy them because they're so bad they're funny."

"That's OK. Thank you for your honesty," said Angela. "It was just an idea. You probably wouldn't need to do many magic tricks for this job anyway."

"We've forgotten one very important question," said Geraldine, and turned to David. "How would you feel about wearing very big shoes?"

David thought for a moment. In a situation like this, complete honesty seemed the only possible course of action. Would he mind wearing very big shoes? No, he wouldn't.

"Very big shoes would be fine," he said.

It was three days after the interview. The postman had just delivered the letter that David now held in his hand. It had the hospital logo on it. Normally when a letter arrived after an interview, he waited until the right moment to open it. If it was good news, he wanted to be able to enjoy the moment. Not that it ever *was* good news. But in this case there was no chance that he'd get the job, not after that weird interview. He casually ripped open the envelope and read:

Dear Mr Turner,
We are pleased to offer you the position of clown/entertainer in our children's section. Please contact me on the telephone number above to discuss your start date.
Yours sincerely,
Angela Landsdown,
Assistant Human Resources Manager

Two years later

"I'm sorry you're leaving us," said Angela. "But thank you very much for all you've done. You're the best clown we've ever had. It's going to be hard to replace you."

"Well, thank *you*," said David. "It's been such a great opportunity for me. I've really learned a lot."

"Good luck with the TV job," said Angela.

"It's only a children's show," said David.

"It's very popular," said Angela. "My kids love it. And I'm sure that's just the start."

"You think so?" said David.

"Yes," said Angela. "I think you'll go far. You've got a natural talent."

b) *Find the words in the text for these definitions. Give lines.*

1. to be angry with: _____

2. company section employing and training people: _____

3. quite young: _____

4. plan of steps to achieve sth: _____

5. paper container in which sb sends a letter: _____

c) *Bring the events in the order in which they happen. There's one extra statement.*

- [ ] David receives a letter.
- [ ] David celebrates the good news.
- [ ] David has to answer weird questions.
- [ ] David has to give his personal details.
- [ ] A hospital invited David for an interview.
- [ ] David is called in for the interview.
- [ ] David will appear on TV.
- [ ] David arrives at the Human Resources Department.

3 Story

d) *Are these statements true, false or not in the text? Tick ✔ the correct answer.*

	true	false	not in the text
1. David has had an interest in creative arts for a long time.			
2. David has been unemployed for quite some time.			
3. There was a misunderstanding at the hospital's Human Resources Department.			
4. David tried to impress the interviewers with his skills.			
5. David doesn't have the talent to be on a TV show.			

e) *Have a closer look at the narrative techniques in the story.*

1. Where's the turning point (give lines)? Explain what happens and why it's the turning point.

   _____

   _____

   _____

2. Name the clues in the story that point towards the turning point.

   _____

   _____

   _____

3. How is humour used in the story? Give an example.

   _____

   _____

   _____

   _____

f) *In your exercise book write a short characterisation of David (about 100 words).*

g) *Your opinion: Do you think the story is funny? Was it surprising for you? With a partner, discuss why you liked / didn't like it.*

WRITING 24 More about David → SB 101; S6–8

*Choose **one** of the following tasks. Write about 150 words in your exercise book.*

1. Write David's application letter for the position in the children's TV show.
2. As a journalist for your school magazine, you write an interview with David about his job as a clown at the hospital.

Focus 2 School days

VOCABULARY

1 School systems → SB 103

a) *Put the words below into the correct category. Each word can only be used once.*

| A-levels | college | elementary education | GCSE | grammar school | high school | primary education | vocational school | secondary education | sixth form college | university |

1. Levels in the educational system: _____

2. Secondary schools: _____

3. Exams to finish secondary school: _____

4. Educational institution after secondary school: _____

b) *For a student exchange, your class prepares a picture gallery. Take or bring a picture showing something typical of German schools. In groups, practise presenting your picture.*

LISTENING

2 School experiences in the US → SB 104; S6–8, S12

A 13–15 🔊

a) *Listen to this live podcast about schools in the US and match the sentence parts. More than one answer can be correct. There's one extra phrase on the right.*

1. Abigail
2. Gavin
3. Jada

a) thinks that there can even be too much pressure in sports.
b) would like more support for students' families.
c) wishes school would teach more than textbook[1] knowledge.
d) prefers to be homeschooled.
e) doesn't feel there's enough free time to do fun stuff.
f) thinks that there's too much emphasis on exams.

b) *Listen to part 1 and complete the information in the grid.*

GPA (= Grade Point _____)	SAT
– _____ grade made up of all grades and _____ of a student's time at school – compares results to that of the students _____	– standardised test towards the end of your _____ – test results are compared to students _____ – main subjects: _____ and _____

[1] textbook ['tekstbʊk] Lehrbuch

sixty-seven **67**

Focus 2

c) *Are these statements true or false? Tick ✔ the correct answer.*

	true	false
1. According to Abigail, preparing for the SAT can influence students' time management skills negatively.	☐	☐
2. Schools want their students to get into good colleges because it improves the school's image.	☐	☐
3. Abigail criticizes that the influence of test results on the students' future lives is too big.	☐	☐

d) *Listen to part 2 and tick ✔ the correct answer.*

1. In Gavin's opinion…
   a) ☐ you can't start preparing for the SAT early enough.
   b) ☐ there's too much homework.
   c) ☐ studying until late at night can be helpful.

2. Gavin plays cricket …
   a) ☐ to improve his chances to get into a good college.
   b) ☐ because he wants to become a professional player.
   c) ☐ for fun.

3. In a *typical* lesson at Gavin's school the students …
   a) ☐ do creative and interactive projects.
   b) ☐ study textbooks or give presentations.
   c) ☐ give lessons to the younger kids.

4. Gavin believes that it's more important to learn …
   a) ☐ how to work with technology rather than just learning how to use it.
   b) ☐ from experience rather than from a teacher.
   c) ☐ basic knowledge rather than specific skills.

e) *Listen to part 3 and complete the text.*

Just like more than _____ other children in the US, Jada is being homeschooled. Jada felt that leaving school was better for her _____ because her state school didn't have very good equipment, and she didn't like the fact that her teachers _____. She also thinks that, because every child _____, children should be educated in a way that considers their inividual needs. Jada doesn't miss the _____ of school because she still has her old friends and is in a _____.

WRITING

f) *Your opinion: Write a comment (about 100 words) for your school magazine about what you would change to improve your school life. Look at the pictures for some ideas.*

Revision C

→ Solutions p. 73

LANGUAGE

1 Free-range → SB 106; G17

You are writing the FAQ of a website of a friend's farm shop which sells free-range meat and eggs. In your exercise book, add the relative clauses to the answers. Some are defining and some are non-defining.

Start: Free-range, which …

1. **Q:** What does 'free-range' mean?
   A: Free-range means that the animals can spend at least some time can refer to meat or eggs
   each day moving freely outside.

2. **Q:** If it says free-range on the packet, can I be sure it's free-range in the packet?
   A: Only meat and eggs from farms can be sold as free-range. are regularly checked by officials

3. **Q:** Where do free-range products come from?
   A: They typically come from local independent farmers. have decided to offer a higher quality product

4. **Q:** Is there a free-range logo?
   A: No. Some supermarket chains have their own free-range logo. are selling more free-range products than ever

5. **Q:** Why are free-range products usually more expensive?
   A: The extra production costs must be passed on to the customer. can be quite high

LANGUAGE

2 A horrible interview → SB 107; G18–20

You applied as an office assistant, but your interview was a total disaster. You send an e-mail to your friend Josie telling her what went wrong. Rewrite the sentences in your exercise book using different forms to add emphasis.

Start: 1. Sadly, my interview didn't go well **at all** …

> Dear Josie,
> (1) Sadly, my interview didn't go well. My bus had been late, so I arrived with a very red face. (2) I noticed that I had sweaty hands only when I had to shake hands with my interviewer! (3) I had a good answer to many questions. (4) But I had trouble answering the question about my weaknesses. What happened next was worse though. (5) I not only poured my glass of water across the table, but I then laughed like crazy. (6) I've never been more embarrassed in my life. (7) Still: I want the job. Hope your applications are going better! See you soon!

VOCABULARY

3 Adventures at sea → SB 107

Your friend Josie got a job on a ship. Complete her e-mail reply. Use synonyms (=), opposites (↔) or other related words (→) for the words in blue.

> Hi! Sorry your interview didn't meet your _____ (→ to expect)! Imagine, my
>
> _____ (→ to apply) for the job on a touristic ship was _____
>
> (→ success). The _____ (= wage) is good. It will be an _____ (= making
>
> you tired) job: I'm going to _____ (→ advertisement) trips to people on board the
>
> _____ (= whole) day. But I hope to have _____ (↔ active) evenings with
>
> _____ (= people you work with) of many different _____ (→ national).
>
> I need to _____ (→ signature) the papers now! Love, Josie

Revision C

LISTENING

4 My kind of company → SB 111; S12

A 16

a) *Listen to different people who were hired¹ by some of California's tech companies talking about their jobs in Silicon Valley. Take notes to complete the grid about the pros and cons according to the speakers.*

who	pros	cons
Speaker 1		
Speaker 2		
Speaker 3		

b) *Listen again. Are these statements true or false? Tick ✔ the correct answer.*

	true	false
1. Because Silicon Valley attracts people from all around the world, the competition there is harder than elsewhere.	☐	☐
2. Employing young people is not good for tech companies in Silicon Valley.	☐	☐
3. To start a tech career as a woman, you need to be hard-working and good-looking.	☐	☐
4. It is just as important to get on well with the people at your company as it is to work hard.	☐	☐

c) *Complete the sentences.*

1. Speaker 1 first came to Silicon Valley for _____ .

2. Speaker 2 is originally _____ .

3. _____ of all scientists and engineers are immigrants.

4. Speaker 3 remembers that some kids _____ _____ .

1 to hire ['haɪə] einstellen

Revision C

LANGUAGE

5 Find the mistakes: Ronaldinho's success story → SB 111; G18

Read the article from a magazine about football star Ronaldinho. Decide if the underlined words or phrases are correct or not. Correct the mistakes.

Ronaldo de Assis Moreira, better (1) <u>known for</u> Ronaldinho, is one of the world's most famous footballers. His mother was (2) <u>nurse</u>, and his father built ship parts. (3) <u>Sad</u>, his father died when Ronaldinho (4) <u>is</u> just eight years old, (5) <u>having left</u> the family with (6) <u>little money</u>. Like many boys in Brazil[1], Ronaldinho and his older brother Roberto dreamed (7) <u>to become</u> professional footballers. When Roberto (8) <u>succeeded at</u> this, the family was (9) <u>fewer poor</u> for a while. (10) <u>Unfortunatly</u>, Roberto's career (11) <u>was ended</u> soon after by (12) <u>a injury</u>. Ronaldinho also showed great skill in football (13) <u>since</u> an early age. Because he (14) <u>has usually been</u> the youngest and smallest player ('-inho' means 'little') in youth club matches, he was given his nickname. He was first noticed (15) <u>from media</u> when he was 13 and scored 23 goals in a match (16) <u>against</u> another youth team. He soon became one of the world's best footballers with a great career. Not only (17) <u>he has entertained</u> (18) <u>millions football fans</u> for many years with his amazing skills, but he (19) <u>has also inspired</u> a whole generation of young footballers from poor social backgrounds.

1. _____

LANGUAGE

6 Mixed bag: A volunteer year in assisted living[2] → SB 111

After school, Paul spent a year volunteering for an assisted living organisation. Complete his report for the organisation's website.

I _____ work without _____ experience. But my boss found many tasks I _____ be given! First, I got office tasks _____ preparing schedules or taking calls while _____ to know the residents. Soon I got much _____ (interesting) duties. You _____ not know that many people with disabilities _____ go to work. So my job was _____ sure they _____ ready on time. I helped people _____ their clothes or assisted wheelchair users _____ the bus. In the evenings, we _____ play games. One experience I _____ was a visit at the cinema with a wheelchair user. The elevator was broken, so we _____ carry him up the stairs! That _____ a lesson: don't go anywhere alone. Thanks to volunteering, I am _____ prejudiced _____ all kinds of people and more certain of my ability _____ well with difficult situations.

[1] Brazil [brəˈzɪl] Brasilien [2] assisted living [əˈsɪstɪd ˈlɪvɪŋ] betreutes Wohnen für Menschen mit Behinderung

Solutions

Unit 1
Page 3, Ex. 2:
1 b); 2 b); 3 a); 4 c); 5 a); 6 c)

Revision A
Page 22, Ex. 1, Lösungsvorschlag:
Dear Carmen,
I'm so excited: We are going on holiday tomorrow! Tomorrow morning, a taxi is going to pick us up and bring us to the airport. Our flight to Auckland leaves at 3 p.m., that means I'll be sitting on the plane by this time tomorrow. I just watched the weather forecast for New Zealand. The weather will be mostly sunny, so I will be spending some time at the beach. But on our first day, we will visit Sky Tower.
I have to go pack now! What are your plans this summer?
Love, (name)

Page 22, Ex. 2:
- **J:** The plot is about some young Aboriginals who decide that if they **don't fight / didn't fight** to keep their identity, they**'ll / will lose / would lose** it. I think learning about Aboriginal culture is very important. Actually, if we **didn't enter** our films in festivals like the Melbourne International Film Festival, a lot of people **wouldn't know** much about it.
- **A:** What kind of film **would you make** if you **had** a big Hollywood budget?
- **J:** I don't think that's very likely! If you**'d / had asked** me that question a few years ago, I**'d / would have said** a big historical drama, but now I'm happy making low-budget art films. I don't want to do anything else.

Page 22, Ex. 3:
Before I worked at the cattle station, I **worked / had worked / been working** as a waiter in Melbourne. And if I **hadn't seen / found** that flyer at my hostel, I **would have never had / got** the idea to work on a cattle station. The first weeks were **extremely / very / especially / really** tough because **the** work was **harder** than expected. The boss **made** us go to work before daylight! The **climatic / weather** conditions were quite harsh, too. I always **wore** a hat to protect **myself / my head** from the sun. However, I enjoyed **riding** around the outback on horseback and I often stopped **to look** at the **outstanding / unique** landscape. Actually, I wish I **had gone / worked** there earlier.

Page 23, Ex. 4, Lösungsvorschlag:
Dear Amrita,
I hope your project is going well! Did you know that there are camels in Australia? When European pioneers started to explore central Australia in the 19th century, they imported the animals from mainly India and Pakistan and used them to transport goods. But soon the problems began: In the 1920s the animals were replaced by trains and cars and lots of camel owners just let their animals free. They thought the camels would just die, but the animals were able to survive and because they didn't have any natural enemies, their number grew quickly. In addition to that, the powerful beef industry in Australia wants to keep the quantity of camel meat low, so the population isn't reduced by the meat production. Today, these wild camels are a big problem in Australia. (There might actually be up to 1.5 million of them!) The camels make it harder for smaller animals to get to food and water and they break into farms. However, the camels are still useful. They are used for tours with tourists through the outback. Some camels are exported to the United Arab Emirates where they are used in races or meat production. Although camel meat is used for burgers and sausages, eating it is not very common in Australia yet.
I hope you find the information useful.
Love, (name)

Page 24, Ex. 5:
1. was
2. the end of the Vietnam War / the Vietnam War had ended
3. extremely difficult
4. had been arrested
5. decided to take
6.–7. correct
8. had imagined
9. correct
10. being attacked / attacks
11. many others
12. were allowed to go
13. really wanted
14. hadn't been able to speak
15. correct
16. might not have chosen
17. hard
18. correct
19. an
20. hasn't been
21. will always remember

Page 24, Ex. 6:
I'm a true New Zealander and I**'ve / have lived / been living** in Queenstown my whole life. **What** I love **most** about New Zealand is **its / the** breathtaking scenery. Even though I**'ve / have been / travelled / gone** to over twenty countries, I think the landscape of New Zealand is **more** beautiful than **any** other. Although I love **exploring / to explore** other countries, I prefer **to travel / travelling** around my **own** country now. There's so **much** to see: beaches, mountains, deserts and rainforests. If that **doesn't convince** you, **then**

maybe New Zealand's rich indigenous culture will. For example, the national rugby team **are / is** the only team **to perform / that perform(s)** a Maori haka before **each / a / every** match. **Unfortunately / However**, racism is still an issue here and people avoid **talking** about it. But all in all, the people of New Zealand are some of **the friendliest** people you **will** ever **meet**.

Revision B
Page 45, Ex. 1:
Not much of the building behind me is left. It was a clothing factory. I was here yesterday **seeing** it **burn** down. At first there was just smoke, but I heard somebody **call** the emergency services. For several minutes I watched people **carrying** clothes from the building. Then the fire suddenly got worse, and I heard a small explosion **break** some windows. **Feeling** the heat of the fire on my skin, I was glad when the firefighters finally arrived. **Fighting** their way through the flames, they managed **to rescue** several people **trapped** inside. The workers in this factory were lucky **to get out** alive, but many others weren't. **Having heard** of similar disasters many times, why haven't we reacted yet? It's obvious that **ignoring** how our clothes are produced means **contributing** to bad working conditions. That's reason enough for me to start **to think / thinking** about where I buy my clothes today.

Page 45, Ex. 2:
Ira: What did Jacob say what needs to be done?
You: Jacob said (that) he wanted the politicians to take action right away. He claimed (that) our planet was in a crisis and that we all had to act in order to survive.
Ira: Did he mention young people or what his goal is?
You: Jacob asked what else young people could do to raise awareness for that problem. He added (that) he hoped for a world that we could still live in in a hundred years.
Ira: What does he plan to do next?
You: Jacob stated that as scientists and activists had been ignored by politicians, he was planning to strike the following week / the week after.

Page 46, Ex. 3a):
1. true
2. false
3. not in the text
4. true

Page 46, Ex. 3b):
1. Delafosse and Erussard's catamaran uses **renewable power only / wind and solar energy** to cross the oceans.
2. The trip from Europe to the Caribbean took **60 days** and covered a distance of **9,000 km**.
3. The crew didn't have to buy **drinking water** because they produced it themselves.
4. **(Many) activists** help to improve the world and to reach **the SDGs** by 2030.

Page 47, Ex. 4:
1. describes
2. have to leave
3. because of
4. refers to
5. correct
6. extremely high
7. becoming
8. much palm oil
9. is used to make
10. is used for
11. correct
12. recent
13. more
14. than
15. Producing
16. correct
17. who live
18. it
19. covers
20. need / needed
21. is interested

Page 47, Ex. 5:
I**'ve / have been** on board the Energy Observer for 50 days now. Sometimes I still **can't** believe I'm really here. I still remember how it all **began / started**. A few years ago, I read about a project that **had been started / organised by** two French guys. They **were building** an emission-free ship at the time **that / which** should **use / run on** the power of the ocean, wind and sun instead of **fossil** fuels. I, **being / as** a diver and scientist, **really / very much** wanted to take part in the project and a year later I got on board! **What** I love **most** about the ship is that if it is cloudy and windless (which **happens** regularly), the motor **can run / runs on** hydrogen for up to six days. Today we **went** diving and saw several large sharks **swimming** just below our ship. The underwater world **keeps** surprising me! I **couldn't** wish for a more interesting job!

Revision C
Page 69, Ex. 1:
1. Free range, **which** can refer to meat or eggs, means that the animals can spend at least some time each day moving freely outside.
2. Only meat and eggs from farms **which / that** are regularly checked by officials can be sold as free range.
3. They typically come from local independent farmers **who / that** have decided to offer a higher quality product.
4. No. Some supermarket chains, **which** are selling more free range products than ever, have their own free range logo.
5. The extra production costs, **which** can be quite high, must be passed on to the customer.

Solutions

Page 69, Ex. 2, Lösungsvorschlag:
2. **Only when** I had to shake hands with my interviewer **did I notice** (that) I had sweaty hands! / **It was only when** I had to … **that** I noticed (that) I had sweaty hands.
3. I **did** have a good answer to many questions.
4. But **it was** the question about my weaknesses **that** I had trouble answering.
5. **Not only did I pour** my glass of water across the table, **but** I then laughed like crazy.
6. **Never have I been** more embarrassed in my life.
7. Still: I **do** want the job.

Page 69, Ex. 3:
Hi! Sorry your interview didn't meet your **expectations**! Imagine, I just got informed that my **application** for the job on a touristic ship was **successful**. The **pay / payment** is good. It will be an **exhausting** job: I'm going to **advertise** trips to people on board the **entire** day. But, I hope to have **lazy** evenings with **colleagues** of many different **nationalities**. I need to **sign** the papers now! Love, Josie

Page 70, Ex. 4a):
Speaker 1:
pros: open place; people from everywhere; companies hire inexperienced but motivated young people; like having young people for direct feedback
cons: hard competition, living there can be expensive

Speaker 2:
pros: lots of curiosity and imagination; having to fight (your way to the top) makes you stronger
cons: harder for immigrants, difficult for women, especially at the beginning of the career; lots of pressure and stress

Speaker 3:
pros: one's personality is important, relaxed atmosphere, easy to fit in
cons: good grades don't count as much, confusing system for a beginner, pressure to work hard

Page 70, Ex. 4b):
1. true
2. false
3. false
4. true

Page 70, Ex. 4c):
1. Speaker 1 first came to Silicon Valley for **a summer job.**
2. Speaker 2 is originally **from Vietnam.**
3. **One third** of all scientists and engineers are immigrants.
4. Speaker 3 remembers that some kids **dropped out of school / continued working for companies in Silicon Valley.**

Page 71, Ex. 5:
1. known as
2. a nurse
3. Sadly;
4. was
5. leaving
6. correct
7. of / about becoming
8. succeeded in
9. less poor
10. Unfortunately
11. correct
12. (an) injury
13. from
14. was usually
15. by the media
16. correct
17. has he entertained
18. millions of football fans
19. correct

Page 70, Ex. 6:
I **started / began (to) (my)** work without **(having) any** experience. But my boss found many tasks I **could** be given! First, I got office tasks **like / such as** preparing schedules or taking calls while **getting** to know the residents. Soon I got much **more interesting** duties. You **may** not know that many people with disabilities **nevertheless / still** go to work. So my job was **to make** sure they **were** ready on time. I helped people **(to) put on** their clothes or assisted wheelchair users **to get on** the bus. In the evenings, we **would / used to** play games. One experience I'**ll never forget / always remember** was a visit at the cinema with a wheelchair user. The elevator was broken, so we **had to** carry him up the stairs! That **taught me / us** a lesson: don't go anywhere alone. Thanks to volunteering, I am **less** prejudiced **against** all kinds of people and more certain of my ability **to deal** well with difficult situations.

Irregular verbs

infinitive	simple past	past participle	German
be [bi:]	was [wɒz]/were [wɜ:]	been [bi:n]	sein
become [bɪˈkʌm]	became [bɪˈkeɪm]	become [bɪˈkʌm]	werden
begin [bɪˈgɪn]	began [bɪˈgæn]	begun [bɪˈgʌn]	beginnen, anfangen
bend [bend]	bent [bent]	bent [bent]	biegen, beugen
bet [bet]	bet [bet]/betted [ˈbetɪd]	bet [bet]/betted [ˈbetɪd]	wetten
bite [baɪt]	bit [bɪt]	bitten [ˈbɪtn]	beißen
blow [bləʊ]	blew [blu:]	blown [bləʊn]	blasen, pusten
break [breɪk]	broke [brəʊk]	broken [ˈbrəʊkn]	(zer-)brechen, kaputt machen
breed [bri:d]	bred [bred]	bred [bred]	züchten, sich vermehren
bring [brɪŋ]	brought [brɔ:t]	brought [brɔ:t]	(mit-)bringen
build [bɪld]	built [bɪlt]	built [bɪlt]	bauen
burn [bɜ:n]	burnt [bɜ:nt]/burned [bɜ:nd]	burnt [bɜ:nt]/burned [bɜ:nd]	brennen
burst [bɜ:st]	burst [bɜ:st]/bursted [ˈbɜ:stɪd]	burst [bɜ:st]/bursted [ˈbɜ:stɪd]	bersten, platzen
buy [baɪ]	bought [bɔ:t]	bought [bɔ:t]	kaufen
catch [kætʃ]	caught [kɔ:t]	caught [kɔ:t]	fangen
choose [tʃu:z]	chose [tʃəʊz]	chosen [ˈtʃəʊzn]	(aus-)wählen
come [kʌm]	came [keɪm]	come [kʌm]	kommen
cost [kɒst]	cost [kɒst]	cost [kɒst]	kosten
cling [klɪŋ]	clang [klæŋ]	clung [klʌŋ]	kleben, klammern
creep [kri:p]	crept [krept]	crept [krept]	schleichen
cut [kʌt]	cut [kʌt]	cut [kʌt]	schneiden
deal [di:l]	dealt [delt]	dealt [delt]	(be-)handeln
dig [dɪg]	dug [dʌg]	dug [dʌg]	graben
do [du:]	did [dɪd]	done [dʌn]	machen, tun
draw [drɔ:]	drew [dru:]	drawn [drɔ:n]	zeichnen, ziehen
dream [dri:m]	dreamt [dremt]/dreamed [dri:md]	dreamt [dremt]/dreamed [dri:md]	träumen
drink [drɪŋk]	drank [dræŋk]	drunk [drʌŋk]	trinken
drive [draɪv]	drove [drəʊv]	driven [ˈdrɪvn]	fahren, treiben
eat [i:t]	ate [et/eɪt]	eaten [ˈi:tn]	essen
fall [fɔ:l]	fell [fel]	fallen [ˈfɔ:lən]	fallen
feed [fi:d]	fed [fed]	fed [fed]	füttern, ernähren

Irregular verbs

infinitive	simple past	past participle	German
feel [fi:l]	felt [felt]	felt [felt]	fühlen
fight [faɪt]	fought [fɔ:t]	fought [fɔ:t]	kämpfen, (sich) streiten
find [faɪnd]	found [faʊnd]	found [faʊnd]	finden
fit [fɪt]	fit [fɪt]/fitted [ˈfɪtɪd]	fit [fɪt]/fitted [ˈfɪtɪd]	passen
fly [flaɪ]	flew [flu:]	flown [fləʊn]	fliegen
forbid [fəˈbɪd]	forbade [fəˈbæd]	forbidden [fəˈbɪdn]	verbieten
forget [fəˈget]	forgot [fəˈgɒt]	forgotten [fəˈgɒtn]	vergessen
forgive [fəˈgɪv]	forgave [fəˈgeɪv]	forgiven [fəˈgɪvn]	vergeben, verzeihen
freeze [fri:z]	froze [frəʊz]	frozen [ˈfrəʊzn]	gefrieren, erstarren
get [get]	got [gɒt]	got [gɒt]/*AE:* gotten [ˈgɒtn]	bekommen, erhalten
give [gɪv]	gave [geɪv]	given [ˈgɪvn]	geben
go [gəʊ]	went [went]	gone [gɒn]	gehen, fahren
grow [grəʊ]	grew [gru:]	grown [grəʊn]	wachsen, anbauen, züchten
hang [hæŋ]	hung [hʌŋ]	hung [hʌŋ]	hängen
have [hæv]	had [hæd]	had [hæd]	haben
hear [hɪə]	heard [hɜ:d]	heard [hɜ:d]	hören
hide [haɪd]	hid [hɪd]	hidden [ˈhɪdn]	(sich) verstecken
hit [hɪt]	hit [hɪt]	hit [hɪt]	schlagen, treffen
hold [həʊld]	held [held]	held [held]	halten
hurt [hɜ:t]	hurt [hɜ:t]	hurt [hɜ:t]	verletzen, sich weh tun
keep [ki:p]	kept [kept]	kept [kept]	(auf-)bewahren, behalten
know [nəʊ]	knew [nju:]	known [nəʊn]	kennen, wissen
lay [leɪ]	laid [leɪd]	laid [leɪd]	legen
lead [li:d]	led [led]	led [led]	führen
lean [li:n]	leant [lent]/leaned [li:nd]	leant [lent]/leaned [li:nd]	lehnen, beugen
leap [li:p]	leapt [lept]/leaped [li:pt]	leapt [lept]/leaped [li:pt]	springen
learn [lɜ:n]	learnt [lɜ:nt]/learned [lɜ:nd]	learnt [lɜ:nt]/learned [lɜ:nd]	lernen
leave [li:v]	left [left]	left [left]	(ver-)lassen
lend [lend]	lent [lent]	lent [lent]	leihen
let [let]	let [let]	let [let]	lassen
lie [laɪ]	lay [leɪ]	lain [leɪn]	liegen
lose [lu:z]	lost [lɒst]	lost [lɒst]	verlieren
make [meɪk]	made [meɪd]	made [meɪd]	machen, tun

Irregular verbs

infinitive	simple past	past participle	German
mean [mi:n]	meant [ment]	meant [ment]	bedeuten, meinen
meet [mi:t]	met [met]	met [met]	treffen
pay [peɪ]	paid [peɪd]	paid [peɪd]	(be-)zahlen
put [pʊt]	put [pʊt]	put [pʊt]	legen, setzen, stellen
read [ri:d]	read [red]	read [red]	lesen
ride [raɪd]	rode [rəʊd]	ridden ['rɪdn]	fahren, reiten
ring [rɪŋ]	rang [ræŋ]	rung [rʌŋ]	klingeln, läuten
rise [raɪz]	rose [rəʊz]	risen ['rɪzn]	aufsteigen, sich erheben
run [rʌn]	ran [ræn]	run [rʌn]	laufen, rennen
say [seɪ]	said [sed]	said [sed]	sagen
see [si:]	saw [sɔ:]	seen [si:n]	sehen
sell [sel]	sold [səʊld]	sold [səʊld]	verkaufen
send [send]	sent [sent]	sent [sent]	senden, verschicken
set [set]	set [set]	set [set]	setzen, einrichten
sew [səʊ]	sewed [səʊd]	sewn [səʊn]/sewed [səʊd]	nähen
shake [ʃeɪk]	shook [ʃʊk]	shaken ['ʃeɪkn]	schütteln
shine [ʃaɪn]	shone [ʃɒn]	shone [ʃɒn]	scheinen
shoot [ʃu:t]	shot [ʃɒt]	shot [ʃɒt]	schießen
show [ʃəʊ]	showed [ʃəʊd]	shown [ʃəʊn]	zeigen
shrink [ʃrɪŋk]	shrank [ʃræŋk]	shrunk [ʃrʌŋk]	schrumpfen, weichen
sing [sɪŋ]	sang [sæŋ]	sung [sʌŋ]	singen
sink [sɪŋk]	sank [sæŋk]	sunk [sʌŋk]	sinken
sit [sɪt]	sat [sæt]	sat [sæt]	sitzen
sleep [sli:p]	slept [slept]	slept [slept]	schlafen
slide [slaɪd]	slid [slɪd]	slid [slɪd]	rutschen
smell [smel]	smelt [smelt]/ smelled [smeld]	smelt [smelt]/ smelled [smeld]	riechen, duften
speak [spi:k]	spoke [spəʊk]	spoken ['spəʊkn]	sprechen
speed up [spi:d]	sped [sped]/ speeded ['spi:dɪd]	sped [sped]/ speeded ['spi:dɪd]	sausen, rasen
spell [spel]	spelt [spelt]/ spelled [speld]	spelt [spelt]/ spelled [speld]	buchstabieren
spend [spend]	spent [spent]	spent [spent]	ausgeben, verbringen
spin [spɪn]	span [spæn]/spun [spʌn]	spun [spʌn]	drehen, spinnen
spit [spɪt]	spat [spæt]	spat [spæt]	spucken

Irregular verbs

infinitive	simple past	past participle	German
spread [spred]	spread [spred]	spread [spred]	(sich) verbreiten
stand [stænd]	stood [stʊd]	stood [stʊd]	stehen
steal [stiːl]	stole [stəʊl]	stolen ['stəʊlən]	stehlen
stick [stɪk]	stuck [stʌk]	stuck [stʌk]	kleben, stecken
sting [stɪŋ]	stung [stʌŋ]	stung [stʌŋ]	stechen
strike [straɪk]	struck [strʌk]	struck [strʌk]	schlagen, zuschlagen
strive [straɪv]	strove [strəʊv]/ strived [straɪvd]	striven [strɪvn]/ strived [straɪvd]	streben, sich bemühen
swear [sweə]	swore [swɔː]	sworn [swɔːn]	schwören, fluchen
sweep [swiːp]	swept [swept]	swept [swept]	fegen
sweel [swel]	swelled [sweld]	swollen ['swəʊlən]/ swelled [sweld]	anschwellen, anwachsen
swim [swɪm]	swam [swæm]	swum [swʌm]	schwimmen
take [teɪk]	took [tʊk]	taken ['teɪkn]	nehmen
teach [tiːtʃ]	taught [tɔːt]	taught [tɔːt]	unterrichten, lehren, beibringen
tell [tel]	told [təʊld]	told [təʊld]	erzählen
think [θɪŋk]	thought [θɔːt]	thought [θɔːt]	(nach-)denken, glauben
throw [θrəʊ]	threw [θruː]	thrown [θrəʊn]	werfen
understand [ˌʌndə'stænd]	understood [ˌʌndə'stʊd]	understood [ˌʌndə'stʊd]	verstehen
upset [ʌp'set]	upset [ʌp'set]	upset [ʌp'set]	aufregen
wake [weɪk]	woke [wəʊk]	woken ['wəʊkn]	wecken, aufwachen
wear [weə]	wore [wɔː]	worn [wɔːn]	anhaben, tragen
win [wɪn]	won [wʌn]	won [wʌn]	gewinnen, siegen
write [raɪt]	wrote [rəʊt]	written ['rɪtn]	schreiben

Text- und Bildquellenverzeichnis

Textquellennachweis
19 From: Last chance to see ©2019 Douglas Adams and Mark Carwardine; **23** Susann Sitzler, Zeit Online, 2014, www.zeit.de; **27** From: Jasper Jones, ©2010 Craig Silvey; **33** „Hinter den Kulissen von Fridays for Future Berlin, Was die jungen Aktivisten treibt und wer sie sind" von Armin Lehmann, Tagesspiegel, 20.09.2020; **43** Anna Turns ©2019 Guardian News&Media Ltd.; **52.1 (Zitat)** Attributed to Farrah Gray; **52.2 (Zitat)** Attributed to George Adams; **52.3 (Zitat)** Atrributed to Robert J. Waldinger; **52.4 (Zitat)** From: Evermore, ©2009 Alyson Nöel; **53** 2019, From www.girls-day.de and www.boys-day.de

Bildquellennachweis
Cover.1 F1online digitale Bildagentur, Frankfurt (Marco Govel/Westend61); **Cover.2** ShutterStock.com RF, New York (Yunsun_Kim); **2.1** ShutterStock.com RF, New York (Globe Turner); **4.1** stock.adobe.com, Dublin (vekidd); **4.2** Alamy stock photo, Abingdon (Andrew Watson); **4.3** ShutterStock.com RF, New York (juancsanchezherrera); **6.1** Getty Images Plus, München (Reinhard Dirscherl); **7.1** Getty Images Plus, München (mihailomilovanovic); **9.1** Getty Images Plus, München (Robin Smith); **9.2** 123rf Germany, c/o Inmagine GmbH, Nidderau (allg); **9.3** ShutterStock.com RF, New York (Heleen Van Assche); **9.4** stock.adobe.com, Dublin (Mirko Vitali); **9.5** stock.adobe.com, Dublin (Yael Weiss); **10.1** stock.adobe.com, Dublin (Stringer Image); **11.1** nach: Australian Government, Bureau of Meteorology; **12.1** Getty Images Plus, München (filadendron); **12.2** Alamy stock photo, Abingdon (Travelscape Images); **15.1** ShutterStock.com RF, New York (WMJ); **15.2** nach: NSW Office of Environment and Heritage, prepared by Roy Morgan Research Ltd, Brisbane, 2016; **15.3** Palmowski, Sven, Barcelona, El Prat de Llobrega; **17.1** ShutterStock.com RF, New York (John Crux); **18.1** stock.adobe.com, Dublin (Anthony Hall); **18.2** Getty Images Plus, München (SharonWills); **18.3** ShutterStock.com RF, New York (Andrey Burstein); **18.4** Getty Images Plus, München (Natali_Mis); **18.5** ShutterStock.com RF, New York (AlexandrMakedonskiy); **19.1** Picture-Alliance, Frankfurt/M. (Minden Pictures); **20.1** Dekelver, Christian, Weinstadt; **21.1** ShutterStock.com RF, New York (Martin Pelanek); **21.2** ShutterStock.com RF, New York (Viktor Hejna); **21.3** ShutterStock.com RF, New York (RICHARD FARAGHER); **21.4** ShutterStock.com RF, New York (Dmitry Pichugin); **21.5** ShutterStock.com RF, New York (kyrien); **21.6** ShutterStock.com RF, New York (Mike-Hubert.com); **22.1** ShutterStock.com RF, New York (Daria_I); **23.1** Ablang, Friederike, Berlin; **23.2** Ablang, Friederike, Berlin; **23.3** Ablang, Friederike, Berlin; **27.1** ShutterStock.com RF, New York (First Class 3D); **29.1** ShutterStock.com RF, New York (GagliardiPhotography); **29.2** ShutterStock.com RF, New York (ESB Professional); **29.3** ShutterStock.com RF, New York (eurobanks); **29.4** ShutterStock.com RF, New York (eurobanks); **29.5** Avenue Images GmbH, Hamburg (StockDisc); **29.6** iStockphoto, Calgary, Alberta (Steve Cole); **30.1** iStockphoto, Calgary, Alberta (Neustockimages); **31.1** Alamy stock photo, Abingdon (ton koene); **32.1** Kramer, Peer, Düsseldorf; **33.1** ShutterStock.com RF, New York (D Busquets); **35.1** TransFair e.V. (Fairtrade Deutschland), Köln; **37.1** www.CartoonStock.com, Bath (Piccolo, Rina); **37.2** ShutterStock.com RF, New York (Inside Creative House); **38.1** Kramer, Peer, Düsseldorf; **38.2** Kramer, Peer, Düsseldorf; **38.3** Kramer, Peer, Düsseldorf; **38.4** Kramer, Peer, Düsseldorf; **40.1** Picture-Alliance, Frankfurt/M. (dpa/Friedel Giert); **41.1** Alamy stock photo, Abingdon (Cavan Images); **44.1** ShutterStock.com RF, New York (Maria Granli Nielsen); **44.2** ShutterStock.com RF, New York (Fevziie); **44.3** Ernst Klett Verlag GmbH, Stuttgart (Eva Kronberg); **44.4** ShutterStock.com RF, New York (trekandshoot); **44.5** 123rf Germany, c/o Inmagine GmbH, Nidderau (William Rodrigues Dos Santos); **45.1** ShutterStock.com RF, New York (jenny on the moon); **45.2** ShutterStock.com RF, New York (Merfin); **45.3** ShutterStock.com RF, New York (CharacterFamily70); **46.1** ShutterStock.com RF, New York (ALX1618); **47.1** ShutterStock.com RF, New York (Maykova Galina); **50.1** Thinkstock, München (omgimages); **51.1** ShutterStock.com RF, New York (Monkey Business Images); **52.1** Avenue Images GmbH, Hamburg (Brand X Pictures); **53.1** ShutterStock.com RF, New York (favorita1987); **53.2** ShutterStock.com RF, New York (favorita1987); **54.1** www.CartoonStock.com, Bath; **54.2** Palmowski, Sven, Barcelona, El Prat de Llobrega; **54.3** Palmowski, Sven, Barcelona, El Prat de Llobrega; **54.4** Palmowski, Sven, Barcelona, El Prat de Llobrega; **55.1** dodotes illustrations, Berlin; **57.1** ShutterStock.com RF, New York (mimagephotography); **57.2** ShutterStock.com RF, New York (grafvision); **59.1** Alamy stock photo, Abingdon (M. Stan Reaves); **60.1** ShutterStock.com RF, New York (VendeDesign); **60.2** U.S. Bureau of Statistics, 2019; **60.3** U.S. Bureau of Statistics, 2019; **66.1** Schwarwel, Leipzig; **67.1** ShutterStock.com RF, New York (Monkey Business Images); **68.1** Thomas Weccard Fotodesign BFF, Ludwigsburg; **68.2** Getty Images Plus, München (SolStock); **68.3** Getty Images, München (View Pictures/Kontributor); **70.1** ShutterStock.com RF, New York (Uladzik Kryhin); **71.1** ShutterStock.com RF, New York (Marco Iacobucci Epp)

Workbook Audios

Track	Chapter	Page	Ex.	Time	Title
A1	Unit 1	4	3	3:22	Where to go in Australia
A2	Unit 1	8	11	2:45	A convict's story
A3	Focus 1	21	2	5:59	On location
A4	Unit 2	30	2	6:27	The five Rs of sustainability
A5	Unit 2	35	10	2:32	Fair trade
A6	Unit 2	41	22	7:03	Behind the wheel
A7–8	Unit 3	57	10	4:12	An interview for an interview
A9–10	Unit 3	58	12	6:50	The internship
A11	Unit 3	61	17	0:49	Safety rules
A12	Unit 3	63	20	2:35	Conduct interviews with applicants and panels
A13–15	Focus 2	67	2	7:49	School experiences in the US
A16	Revision C	70	4	3:29	My kind of company

Schülerbuch Audios

Track	Chapter	Page	Ex.	Time	Title
A1–6	Unit 1	28		13:58	Nona and me
A7	Focus 1	32	1	2:54	A blog article about New Zealand
A8	Text smart 1	44	4	4:37	A very short short story
A9–15	Unit 2	66		13:06	The Carbon Diaries 2015
A16–21	Unit 3	96		17:21	The Giver
A22	Focus 2	105	7	2:39	Harry Potter at Hogwarts
A23–27	Extra line	124		7:20	Claire's Devil
A28–34	Extra line	127		16:25	A flooded city
A35–40	Extra line	131		14:29	Kahu and the whales